AN
ENORMOUS
RECKLESS
BLUNDER

THE STORY OF THE
LEWIS CHEMICAL WORKS

Ali Whiteford

ISLANDS BOOK TRUST

Published in 2017 by the Islands Book Trust
www.theislandsbooktrust.com

ISBN: 978-1-907443-74-9
© Ali Whiteford

Lyrics from 'Tinsel Show' by Karine Polwart reproduced courtesy of Karine Polwart
Extract from *I Can't Stay Long* by Laurie Lee reproduced by permission of Curtis Brown Group Ltd on behalf of the Laurie Lee Partnership. © Laurie Lee, 1975

Islands Book Trust
Laxay Hall
Laxay
Isle of Lewis
HS2 9PJ
Tel: 01851 830316

Typeset by Raspberry Creative Type
Front cover image by Mairi Mackenzie
Printed and bound by Martins the Printers, Berwick upon Tweed

To the peat cutters of Lewis;
past, present and future

Contents

Author's Note

This story is presented in three parts:

> i) The background to Caunter and Matheson as individuals and an exploration as to how they became associated through business, science and politics as well as how they ended up in Lewis.

> ii) The social situation on Lewis when Matheson arrived and events nationally – political, scientific and commercial – which led to the formation of the Lewis Chemical Works.

> iii) The history of the Lewis Chemical Works: the introduction of important players; the planning, construction and development of the different sites; the relationships between the various characters involved; and the aftermath for the people concerned, focussing on Matheson.

When quoting from Donald Morison's manuscript, the grammar and spelling have been kept as originally written so that his voice may be heard.

Acknowledgements

It is some forty years since I first became aware of the one-time existence of the Lewis Chemical Works. During those years, naturally, many people who had an influence on the production of this history have passed away. Roddy Grant – late teacher at Stornoway Primary School – introduced me to Donald Morison's manuscript on the history of the Lewis Chemical Works and, being a keen student of the history of chemistry and of Victorian engineering, it pressed all the right buttons; we spent days tramping the moors to find the location of the works. Frank Thompson provided helpful advice and was a source of inspiration and encouragement, kindling enthusiasm for pursuing the story: 'It would be a pity if the story of the Chemical Works was not more widely known'. Iain Mitchell's energy and practical enthusiasm for the Lewis Chemical Works were an effective driving force for pursuing this publication. The historians James Shaw Grant and Donald MacDonald searched their files and provided encouragement, as did Donald Morison's grandson, Donald Morrison of Kingussie. Duncan MacLeod of Garrabost was a source of knowledge from an older generation and Robin MacKenzie of Stornoway asked interesting questions. Peter Cunningham dug up information about the Garrabost brickworks and Alasdair MacIver of Milngavie provided recollections and tales of the brickworks from the early part of the twentieth century.

Malcolm MacDonald, Cathie Smith, Willie Foulger and Ken Galloway of the Stornoway Historical Society have provided knowledge, encouragement and advice, often pointing me in the right direction when lost. Carol Knott, archaeologist, brought the lie-of-the-land to life on a field visit to the site of the Creed works and in her subsequent documentation of the trip.

Residents of Point have shown much interest in the industrial history of the area; Graham Morrison of the Garrabost Mill gave readily of his time to wield the shovel and uncover pieces of railway line, sleepers or other artefacts. Jessie Leary, also of Garrabost, recalled the happy days of her youth at the peat bank and Norman MacLeod of Knock provided an interesting description of island methods of house-building in the early twentieth century. Alasdair Macleod of Swordale has been a constant source of advice and of encouragement to put pen to paper for many years; his appetite for 'going to the peats' is topped only by his prowess as a chef.

Bill Scott of St Andrews, great-grandson of Donald Morison, opened his family files and provided a clear photo of the stone-mason along with interesting background material and a passion for the tale to be told. After years of searching, my patience was rewarded when Anne Bligh of the excellent Old Ashburton website put me in contact with Ros Fletcher of Angus who came up with a lovely grainy photo of her grandfather's cousin's grandfather – Henry Caunter.

David Crabbe, former Technology lecturer at the Open University, has shared both his enthusiasm for Scottish industrial history and his researches over the years. He has cast an objective eye like a microscope over the manuscript of this work and many of his suggestions for changes and additions have been included.

Library services have been essential for carrying out research, both on and offline. The staff at Stornoway Library, past and present, have always been unfailing in their assistance, patience and knowledge when dealing with sometimes obscure requests, as have the staff of the

Stornoway Pier and Harbour Commission and the Stornoway Trust who gave full access to their archives. The many librarians and archivists at the National Register of Archives, the Royal Pharmaceutical Society, the Royal Geographical Society, the Royal Society, the Royal Society of Chemistry, the British Association for the Advancement of Science, the Chemical Society, the Royal Dublin Society, the University of Giessen, Queen's University Belfast, the University of St Andrews, the University of Kansas, Wick Carnegie Library, the Athenaeum, the Mitchell Library in Glasgow, the Royal Albert Memorial Museum and Art Gallery Exeter, the Devonshire Association, Inverness Library, the Royal Commission for the Ancient and Historical Monuments of Scotland, Museum nan Eilean and the MacAulay Institute for Soil Research who rapidly provided information, help and advice in response to many requests, are too numerous to name individually.

The Islands Book Trust have provided the opportunity for me to finally get this intriguing story out there into the world of print with little fuss.

My wife Aileen – no mean thrower of peats – has listened patiently to my musings and bletherings about things peat for most of her life, roaming the moors with unfailing patience and fortitude in search of apparently uninspiring bumps in the ground and bits of rusty metal. My daughter, Eilidh took many of the photos, painted diagrams and kindly typed the original manuscript with speed and accuracy.

Thank you to all, including those I have forgotten to mention. Any errors are all my own responsibility.

Ali Whiteford
Garrabost

Prologue

'Lewis; a peat floating in the Atlantic'

To the traveller of forty years ago standing on the deck of the ferry 'Clansman', bound for the Isle of Lewis, the presence of land was apparent long before arriving at the quay in Stornoway. The rich and unique peat-reek of accumulated Lewis domestic fires, wafted across the waters of the Minch by the prevailing westerlies, would herald the approaching island. A visit to the island in the spring would witness the moorland being transformed; browns and greens, yellows, oranges and whites giving way to black as peats were cut, thrown, lifted, barrowed, gathered and stacked ready for taking home. For centuries the peat lands of Lewis have been essential for man to exist and thrive in the harsh environment, providing the main source of energy for keeping the house warm and the pot hot.

Things were soon to change. Within the space of a few years the availability of cheap central-heating oil provided an easy alternative to the hard toil of winning the peat. A new generation, with changing expectations and lifestyles, was to all but abandon the ancient tradition of reaping the bountiful fuel supply which the moorland offered, dousing

1

the fires and locking away that tantalising smell. The moorland birds and blackface sheep aren't much disturbed nowadays except by fishermen or the occasional surveyor or engineer working on wind-turbine installations. With the realisation of the possibilities of wind power and the proposed National Grid connection, Hebridean sources of energy other than peat are being tapped for the energy-hungry twenty-first century.

Peat has attracted the power industry world-wide for decades: Sweden, Finland, Russia and Ireland have well-developed industries producing energy from peat. Attempts to develop the peat bogs of Scotland have been made; as recently as 1977 plans were being considered for a peat-fired power station to be built in Stornoway with quick-growing alder and birch wood as a back-up fuel grown on the land drained by the peat harvesting, but to no avail.

This was not the first attempt to exploit the peat-bogs of Lewis. Over 150 years ago – as with today – the search for new energy sources was underway and led to a remarkable attempt to exploit the bogs, by extracting paraffin from the peat using the process of distillation. The Lewis Chemical Works (LCW), which covered many acres on three separate sites, was established in 1857 by Henry Caunter, an agent for James Matheson, the proprietor of Lewis, whose intention was to develop the natural resources of Lewis and thus provide employment for islanders. Matheson was an extremely rich and controversial merchant who had made his fortune trading in the Far East. He was a man motivated by knowledge, especially science and its application to the technological Industrial Revolution, which at that time was at full-steam. By 1874 the LCW was failing and closed, unable to keep up with market forces, but it has left its scars, in the form of a very large, important archaeological site which testifies to Scotland's industrial heritage.

Only two accounts of the history of the Lewis Chemical Works appear to exist. In 1895 Donald Morison, a native of Stornoway, who built and later became the operating foreman of the Works, wrote a manuscript intriguingly entitled 'The Beginning and the End of the Lewis Chemical Works, 1857 – 1874'. In this work, written twenty years or so after the demise of the LCW, Morison relates the technical and operational development of the project as well as describing the characters, warts and all, of the main players in the saga. He saw things through the patient eye of the student of human nature and left no stone unturned, excepting one. It is a passionate document.

In 1862 a paper, entitled 'On the Manufacture of Hydrocarbon Oils, Paraffin etc from Peat', was read at the Cambridge meeting of the British Association for the Advancement of Science by Dr Benjamin Horatio Paul. Paul had been the development chemist at the Lewis Chemical Works from 1858 to 1862, by which time it was becoming a successful venture, creating income from the sale of Lignole lighting oil and enabling James Matheson to begin to offset the vast sums of money he was ploughing into the project. Paul's paper gives a blow-by-blow account of the then current state of peat distillation, of the business plan and of the construction and development of the Lewis Chemical Works. Paul's paper is very objective and deals with substance, as would be expected of a scientist, as well as with the economics of the process, which was part of his responsibility as managing partner. This contrasts well with Morison's informal, subjective approach which concentrates on the characters and their changing relationships as the works were developed.

Morison's and Paul's assessments of the Lewis Chemical Works agree, but for events post-1862, following the departure of Paul, we have to rely on Morison's account; though there is no reason to doubt his word. Morison reveals a world where business management practice, commercial venture and scientific research take on a new light, with results that defied the opportunities presented at the time. Demand for the products of peat distillation was high and the markets appeared broad and endless as the peat-bogs providing the raw material for the process.

Nowadays there is an expectation or even a demand for science to provide for the needs of society, but in the mid-nineteenth century scientists were free to pursue at their leisure whatever took their curiosity; society was happy to reap the benefits as they were presented. If a project looked as if it might succeed people were happy to go along with it; if it failed then someone else would try. Backers were always lurking, waiting to make a fast buck and were not slow to seize the opportunities offered by the new discoveries. Trying to turn the alluring contents of test-tubes into a commercial product could be a ruinous affair but the markets were open for all to try.

Although the commercial success of the Lewis Chemical Works is dubious, it provided islanders with desperately needed employment at a time when paid work was scarce after the failures of both fisheries and harvests and the potato famines of the 1840s.

When set against the developing industrial scene of the mid-nineteenth century, the saga of the Lewis Chemical Works reveals a back-story as intriguing as that of Henry Caunter's industrial adventure. It is a story full of hope, incident, drama, farce and pathos inhabited by scoundrels, the curious, noble gentry, academics and the men of Lewis, some of whom moved in unexpected circles. It is a tale of toil and strife, of success and failure, of the adventure of enterprise, but, above all, a tale of man's quest to improve himself and society, which seems to drive the exploitation of natural resources.

4

The fascinating history of the Lewis Chemical Works, is summed up in the words of David Crabbe, a retired O.U. lecturer in Technology as 'one of the most enchantingly bizarre episodes of Scottish Industrial history'.

PART ONE

The Journey to Lewis

Chapter One

Henry Caunter

'Take two insults rather than give one'
- Henry Caunter

At the northern end of Francis Street in Stornoway on the Isle of Lewis, stands the small, nineteenth century Episcopalian Church of St Peter's. In the graveyard stands an impressive, six-foot, granite obelisk at the head of a stone-kerbed gravesite. The base of the obelisk bears a brass plate carrying the inscription 'Henry Caunter 1808 – 1881', the whole giving the impression that Henry Caunter had been an important man within the community. Indeed, in 1861 Slater's Commercial Directory for Scotland recorded in the Stornoway entry under the heading 'Gentry and Clergy': 'Caunter, Henry, Esq, Glen Villa'. (Glen Villa is called Glen House today, a substantial cottage standing at the corner of Willowglen Road, opposite the Caberfeidh Hotel in Stornoway).

Caunter was an intelligent and educated man of some standing in his native Ashburton; a man with a deep interest in science. Indeed, his photograph, although blurred, reflects

9

an engaging curiosity. On his first visit to Lewis in August 1845 Henry Caunter was an important guest at a dinner given in honour of James Matheson, who had just become the proprietor of the island. The banker Roderick Morrison gave Caunter a welcoming and encouraging introduction:

> I have great pleasure in proposing the health of a gentleman who has so kindly appeared amongst us this night as a guest in connection of the constituency of Ashburton – I mean Mr Caunter. Since his arrival on the island he has been marked for his intelligence and kindly deportment; and we trust that in the course of his scientific researches, its hidden treasures will be brought to light, and thereby add to his own large stock of knowledge.

Donald Morison, a stonemason and native of Stornoway, grew to know Caunter well and in his writings gives an excellent, even intimate, description of a talented man of the times, full of hope for things to come:

> Mr Caunter was a gentleman of extensive knowledge and sanguine temperament, possessed with an ardent desire to theorise and experiment with the hope of making a discovery hitherto unknown in the Arts and Sciences. A gifted speaker able to convince his hearers however sceptical – a first class portrait painter, a geologist and antiquarian of high standing. Mr Caunter was always on the lookout for fossils of which he had a large collection representing the evolution of coal, ice, flint, stone, bronze and other prehistoric periods, on all he could

descant with ease. A robust bodied gentleman
16½ stone weight, subject to gout in his feet.

Caunter was a free-and-easy, down-to-earth character, as a correspondent of the Inverness Courier described him whilst on a visit to the island in the mid-1860s, 'I found him to be an Englishman with the bluff, ready, off-hand manner of his countrymen, very civil, attentive and communicative.'

He was also an important man in the history of the Lewis Chemical Works; the man with the enthusiasm and drive to get the project off the ground and take it to a stage where it could be developed commercially by those with the money and the know-how. However, he was also the man who presided over disastrous management decisions and missed business opportunities; not only those revealed by the twenty-twenty vision of hindsight but even those apparent at the time. He could well be credited with being the inspiration for Donald Morison's manuscript, 'The Beginning and the End of the Lewis Chemical Works 1857-1874'.

Henry Caunter started his life a long way from Stornoway, in the sunny county of Devon in the south-west of England. On the 15th November 1808, in the town of Ashburton in South Devon, a son was born to John and Grace Caunter, who had him christened Henry on 14th March 1809, a brother for Richard, George, Charles, Mary and John. His father was a wealthy wool merchant and mill-owner producing serge blankets and the Caunters were an established family in Ashburton. Henry's father died when he was just fifteen but the young Henry was well provided for, with support and maintenance until he was twenty-one, after which he inherited money, land and properties in and around Ashburton. He was a wealthy young man with prospects.

For centuries Ashburton had been an important centre of the woollen trade. At the time of Henry's birth the manufacture of serge – a double worsted fabric – was a cottage industry, but that was soon to change. In 1817 John Caunter built a water-powered yarn-spinning mill in the town, the first such mill in the Ashburton Water. So Henry grew up in a time of great change, with the industrial revolution well under way – the steam engine had developed to such an extent that, by the 1820s, Goldsworthy Gurney's steam coach was challenging the horse-drawn coaches on the road between Ashburton and Totnes – and he was in the right place to literally see the cogs of industry turning at close quarters. Caunter's formative years were also a time of huge development in the academic world, where the study of science was in its Romantic era. Scientific progress was rapid and exciting as newly discovered facts and theories became more accessible to the public. In 1831 Murray's Family Library made available works by the chemist Humphrey Davy, the geologist Charles Lyell and Brewster's 'Life of Sir Isaac Newton'. Henry led a privileged and comfortable life, allowing him to develop an interest in things scientific, notably the new study of geology and fossils, or 'figured stones' as they were then known. Science was to be influential in shaping his life. His parents undoubtedly encouraged an all-round education, as Henry grew into a gifted singer, musician and artist, talents which he developed and maintained to a professional level. His talents, along with his business and political interests, ensured that he became a pivotal member of the commercial and social life of the community.

On 15th October 1835 Henry was married to Sarah Fulford of nearby Crediton and a family soon followed. Young Sarah was born in 1837 and a sister, Alice, followed in 1840. His joy in his growing family was soon shattered, as tragedy struck the following year when Sarah died from pneumonia, aged just twenty-seven. To cope with this loss the family became dispersed. Young Sarah stayed with her mother's family in Ashburton while Alice, by 1851, was attending a small boarding-school in Edinburgh run by her Aunt Eliza, who was married to Alexander MacColl of the East India Company. Although apart, the family remained close.

Back in the 1840s, Henry led a full and busy life. With his musical talents he taught the flute, developing a reputation as a teacher that was to be remembered fifty years later. He was the leader of the Ashburton Glee club, where he performed with his brother John; 'worthy, talented and truly harmonious gentlemen,' reported the local press. He was also president of the Ashburton Madrigal Society, was a leading light in the Ashburton Subscription Concerts and was a popular entertainer at civic dinners.

Developing his artistic skills, he became a portrait painter of some renown. Two of his pictures are in the care of the National Trust, hanging in Bradley Manor in South Devon, whilst a third is to be found in the Royal Albert Memorial Museum in Exeter. This latter picture is a portrait of Abraham Cann, the Devon-style wrestling champion, which received the attention of the press when first exhibited in 1847.

Henry's love of science led him to communicate its fascination to a wider public. He gave lectures to the South Devon Geological and Mineralogical Society, the Mental Improvement Society and the Totnes Mechanics Society on such topics as 'Meteorology', 'Geology', 'Astronomy' and 'Atmosphere – its effects on animal and vegetable life'.

At the time of Sarah's death, Henry was a serge and wool merchant working in the family mill with his brother Richard, responsible for marketing a range of woollen cloths.

In the early 1830s Ashburton enjoyed a comfortable prosperity, as its mills sold serge to the East India Company for trading with the Chinese, however in 1833 the East India Company changed its policy and there followed a rapid decline in the centuries-old industry of the town as the Company bought from the rival Yorkshire mills. Henry saw the writing on the wall and in the mid-1840s had a career change; following his geological inclinations he turned his energy and attention to mining. By the beginning of the 1850s Henry's brother Richard and his wife Mary were still running the family mill, employing four hundred workers but only the patronage of a few wealthy traders kept the mill wheels turning for a further decade. So Henry bailed out of trading in soft material to enter the world of harder stuff.

Besides producing wool, Ashburton had, since the 1100s, been an important centre for the mining of tin and other metals such as copper and iron, which had been mined since Roman times. In 1328 it was created one of the Devon 'stannary' towns for the recording of tin and by the early nineteenth century Devon and Cornwall had become the most important tin and copper mining areas worldwide. Along with fellow Ashburtonian, Robert Palk, Henry Caunter managed several tin and copper mines, including the West Beam and Silver Brook mines in the vicinity of Ashburton, from the late 1840s until at least 1853. At this time the two men were joint secretaries of the South Devon Geological and Mineralogical Society.

It was probably during this period of his life that Henry first encountered the distillation of peat, the process that was to engage his energies to the full at the Lewis Chemical Works a decade later. In Devon, the process was used to produce charcoal for the smelting of the metal ores to produce the pure metal; the peat was plentiful on the vast

Dartmoor which dominates South Devon. Sadly for Henry, the fortunes of tin and copper mining were starting to decline by the mid-1850s and by 1859 there was a major slump in the market as cheaper overseas deposits were exploited. An optimist, Henry was not downcast and in 1857 he made a bold decision to leave Ashburton for a new life at the other end of the country, in the Isle of Lewis where the peat lay thick and wide.

Besides all his other interests and commitments, Henry, along with his brother Richard, had become a leading light in the Devon political scene, shouting well for the Liberals. The Reform Act of 1832 had brought about a change in the voting system for the election of MPs. This changed the balance of power away from the landed gentry, who were no longer able to hold the Ashburton seat as other interests gained power. As HJ Hanham, Professor of Politics at Edinburgh University explained;

> In 1833 and 1834, the Liberal serge makers headed by Richard and Henry Caunter, with their employees and dependants, joined other reformers in a sweeping attack on the last relic of the 'ancien regime' in Ashburton. The old practices were challenged in a series of court cases and Richard and Henry Caunter succeeded in obtaining control over the nomination of the Portreeve, the bailiff and the jury.

The ancient title of Portreeve-of-the-Bore represents a civic post awarded to an Ashburtonian, latterly similar to the position of town clerk. In the twelfth century he was the head of the community, with much power and influence over many people and institutions, stopping short of the power of life and death. He dealt with all community matters requiring judgement, the truthful assessment of financial dealings and the characters of those involved in them. By the time Henry was elected to the post in 1851, the duties had become much diluted but still required a man of tact and diplomacy. Ironically, the assessment of character in financial matters was to prove an Achilles' heel for Henry in later years.

The Devon Liberal Association was formed in 1837 and Henry became very involved in its activities; so much so that, the following year, he was in court charged with riot and assault. The charge was instigated by the rival Tory party who had just lost the election, but was later dismissed by the judge who indicated that it was, 'a most idle prosecution and should never have come to court.'

A celebration dinner held in a lavishly decorated marquee with 300 guests was held in Henry's honour with toasts, speeches, music and song. By the time Charles Rushington, the elected liberal Member for Ashburton, rose to speak about Henry, the assembled throng were in a relaxed and receptive mood, having toasted everyone from Queen Victoria, her family, the Government and the Armed Forces, down to the populace:

> Is he a man likely to commit an outrage? Is he a man likely to injure a single living soul? You know of his kindness of heart, you know his excellent moral worth, you know his attachment to science and literature: of all men in the world he would be the last to join in turbulence and riot. On the trial, evidence was born to one phrase of his which would do honour to the judgement and expressions of the most enlightened moralist, a phrase which was stated on oath again and again and which has not as far as I am aware been gain-sayed by the

other side [Tories]. 'Gentlemen', he said, 'take two insults rather than give one.'

Henry wasn't just a peace-loving man of action in the Liberal party, he was a man of stirring words. Although there is no verbatim record of his speech, The North Devon Journal of March 9th 1843 marked an unlikely but important date for the Lewis Chemical Works. It was the day on which Henry proposed, in an eloquent speech, that the fit and proper person to represent the borough of Ashburton as a Member of Parliament in the House of Commons in the forthcoming election was a certain James Matheson.

Chapter Two

James Matheson the Merchant

'A man of considerable foresight'
Alan Reid, Director Matheson & Co.

'An arrogant, stupid man'
The Duke of Wellington

James Nicholas Sutherland Matheson, the second of seven siblings, was born in Lairg, Sutherland, on 19th November 1796, the son of Captain Donald Matheson, a tacksman farmer and Catherine Mackay, daughter of Rev Thomas Mackay. James was given a thorough education; from Inverness Royal Academy he went south to Edinburgh High School and subsequently to Edinburgh University. Aged seventeen, he went further south to London to seek his fortune, starting a career in commerce where opportunism was seen as a virtue. Matheson next struck out east, to Calcutta where he worked in his uncle's counting house of Messrs MacIntosh and Co., learning the ropes as a Free Merchant. In 1815, at age nineteen, he ventured further east to China and, for the next thirteen years developed a number of trading partnerships, making contacts and fuelling his business acumen, eventually leading to the formation of the trading house of Jardine, Matheson and Company.

William Jardine was a fellow Scot and native of Dumfriesshire who had gone out east as a ship's surgeon. The two men met socially in 1820 and as local Lewis historian Sandy Matheson suggests, Jardine with his local experience, pointed James Matheson in the direction of Canton where Matheson established a trading business. Jardine had been developing a lucrative side-line in trading whilst practicing as a surgeon and the friendship between the two developed such that, in 1828, they became business partners, leading to the formation in 1832 of the trading house of Jardine, Matheson and Company. The relationship between the two was described by Alan Reid, a director of the London firm of Matheson & Co. in the 1950s, in *The Thistle and the Jade*:

> James Matheson had a great respect for Jardine and usually deferred to his greater experience and judgement (Jardine was twelve years older than Matheson) although he himself could be pretty opinionated. Matheson was probably the more widely read of the two and a fervent follower of Adam Smith: one can almost hear the soft Highland voice preaching the gospel of Free Trade in the dining room of the factory at Canton.

Trading was brisk as Matheson sought out new trading ports in China, which at that time had limited trading facilities. They were the first trading company to send tea from China to England following the end of the trade monopoly by the East India Company in 1834. To pay for the tea, the traders sold opium to the Chinese, obtained from the Indian poppy crops.

At that time, the Western world saw opium as a benign, albeit habit-forming, substance, taken in water or alcohol as the drink laudanum, when it was used as a pain reliever, a sleeping draught and to quieten children. When William MacGillivray, that pioneering ornithologist and naturalist from the village of Northton in the Isle of Harris, left Aberdeen University in August 1817 to walk home to the Hebrides, he kept a diary in which he recorded all that he took with him and that he saw on the journey. In it he lists the contents of his baggage and, along with paints, crayons, compass, razor, buttons, a flute, gunpowder and so on, he took some opium, no doubt to ease his aching bones after a day tramping the highways and byways.

To the Chinese, opium meant something quite different; they smoked the substance for its hallucinatory effects. To them it was a habit-forming, life-destroying drug which permeated and ravaged Chinese society. Jardine and Matheson were not discouraged in this trade by the Government as the buying of the opium actually created revenue for the East India Company, but dealing in such a contentious commodity was bound to cause friction sooner or later. The Chinese authorities naturally banned its import but such was the importance of the opium trade in the commercial world that all hell broke loose as stock markets fell and businesses collapsed. Matheson's driving force in this hostile piece of merchant venturing was a belief in Free Trade which seemed to know no bounds. His zealous trading had opened up new markets and Jardine and Matheson were making a vast fortune, so they used their knowledge of the area to petition and influence the British Government. The subsequent gun-boat diplomacy led to outright war as the Opium Wars of the 1840s saw British might prevail over Chinese wisdom.

Matheson was not without business talent. Alan Reid's description of him continues:

James, considerate as well as knowledgeable, was a great asset to the small self-contained community [Canton]. The nearest lawyer was in Calcutta but he did his best to help friends with legal problems. He was enthusiastic about new ideas and was an avid reader of scientific books. He was knowledgeable in Spanish and this proved helpful in developing Jardine Matheson business in Latin America, the Philippines and Europe. He was a man of considerable foresight and in 1836, some years before the event, he proposed the acquisition of Hong Kong island as a 'factory for British, and notably Scottish, traders'.

180 years later the name of Jardine Matheson is still associated with Hong Kong. When Jardine retired to England in 1839, Matheson – who was known in the firm as 'Uncle James' – persuaded him not to remove his name from the firm, his foresight allowing the enterprise to flourish under its well-established banner.

Back in England Jardine entered politics and found a quick route to the House of Commons as the elected member for Ashburton. The Chinese campaign against opium smuggling had had a devastating effect on the fortunes of Ashburton. When the East India Company trade monopoly with China fell in 1834, the merchants of Ashburton started to deal with Jardine Matheson but, with the advent of war, trade ceased and the prosperity of the town declined. The borough of Ashburton sent a representative to Westminster and so the selection of MP would depend upon the latter's ability to promote the export of the town's serge.

Jardine was subsequently elected as MP in June 1840 and in 1841, he placed orders for cloth with Richard Caunter,

Henry's brother, simply to keep the workforce employed over the winter. Tragically, the support was short-lived as Jardine died in February 1843. His seat was offered to James Matheson who had returned to England in 1841 on medical advice and whose reputation gave hope to the people of Ashburton. It is in these highly unlikely beginnings that the emergence some years later of the Lewis Chemical Works became possible.

Matheson returned to England an extremely rich man, having imbibed the contemporary wisdom that Far East traders should make money as quickly as possible since the mortality rate amongst them was high. His return was not without controversy; the war had left 25,000 Chinese and sixty-nine Britons dead and was once described as 'the most disgraceful war in history'. Matheson had been influenced by Jardine and probably by his attitudes. As Brian Inglis describes in *The Opium Wars*: 'Business affairs as far as Jardine was concerned were in a separate living compartment, divorced from the morality of the home'.

In his novel *Sybil*, published in 1837, Disraeli alluded to Matheson as 'One MacDrug fresh from Canton with a million of opium in each pocket, denouncing corruption and bellowing Free Trade', but, as Peter Cunningham points out 'this caricature in a novel published one year after Matheson's purchase of Lewis and before the building of the Castle, could equally have fitted William Jardine who opposed Disraeli in politics.'

The Lewis historian, Frank Thompson, puts the ventures of Matheson and Jardine into some kind of perspective: 'Perhaps, to be kind, we should look at them in the context of their own times, an almost impossible task for us in our times.'

Matheson's wealth was vast. Some twenty years later, the gossip columns of the London press reported on a town ball which had tongues wagging:

I am told that the blaze of diamonds at the late ball has never been paralleled in modern times. Her Royal Highness' dress was dazzlingly brilliant but she was outshone by some of the City dames. Lady Matheson, wife of Sir James, formerly of the firm of Jardine Matheson and Co., the great China merchants, carried about with her a dozen respectable fortunes.

So when he returned to Britain Matheson proceeded to spend. He took up residence in a grand mansion in fashionable Cleveland Row in the city of Westminster. He was to name the property 'Stornoway House', the name by which it is still known today, although it is no longer a dwelling house. A few years later, in 1847, he purchased a country house to go with his town house. Southhill Park, in the town of Bracknell in Berkshire, is a beautiful Georgian mansion built in 1760 which today is used as an arts centre. He had previously, in 1840, purchased the estate of Achany in Sutherland, the family home, but was not yet ready to move north.

With the death of Jardine, the Devon Liberals approached Matheson with the same hope that he would be able to regenerate the almost redundant serge industry. Initially Matheson declined the Liberals' advances; his eyes were still on the Far East where conditions were causing problems for traders. Casualties of the Opium Wars included merchants from Bombay (now Mumbai), with whom Jardine Matheson had traded for a number of years. They had suffered large losses as a result of the conflict and were seeking compensation from the British Government. This required influence within the British Government. On 3rd March 1843 Matheson wrote to his friend and long-time business associate, Sir Jamsetjee Jejeebhoy: 'On its being presented to me that my presence in the House of Commons might be of use to the Opium Compensation Cause, I could no longer hesitate in submitting to all the sacrifice of personal inconvenience etc which it entails upon me.'

One wonders if Matheson was phased by the speed at which his situation changed. The day before Matheson wrote the letter – on Thursday 2nd March – he was in Devon attending a meeting of the Devon Liberals at which he was formerly adopted as the prospective Member of Parliament for Ashburton. On Saturday 4th March he went public in the Western Times:

> The unanimous resolution passed at a crowded and influential meeting of the electors of the Borough, last evening, approved my Political Principles and the numerous assurances of support I have already received, embolden me to announce myself as a candidate for your suffrage at the approaching election. I present myself to you as the friend and former partner of your late lamented member, Mr Jardine. My Political Opinions are favourable to every measure of practicable and progressive Reform and I profess myself the zealous and ardent friend of Civil, Religious and Commercial freedom. My mercantile connections will, I trust, enable me to promote the prosperity of the Staple Trade of your Town, and if returned as your representative, it will be my earnest endeavour to discharge with zeal and assiduity every duty attached to so honourable and important a trust.

He was telling the voters what they wanted to hear and needed to know; they did not need to know about opium compensation. The following Tuesday, March 7th 1843, the election took place and Matheson was duly elected as Member of Parliament for Ashburton with a majority of forty-five, the largest ever recorded for the seat. The Liberals were triumphant and in May Matheson was guest at a dinner given in his honour by his election committee. According to the Western Times correspondent, he cut a dash:

> If fortune hath done much for Mr Matheson, nature hath done more. A man who stands six feet high in his fleecy hosiery, and who in breadth of chest and cleanness of limb shows the possession of full corporeal vigour – whose face beams with the most perfect *bonhomie*, and whose manners are frank, and his whole bearing manly and generous – would, as a bachelor present any time a dangerous customer to the peace of a quiet ancient borough.

So Matheson found himself with a new role in life. Freed from the stresses and strains of the all-consuming world of commerce, he could express his humanity by putting his energies into public works, into spending rather than amassing piles of money, into philanthropy and into indulging his own interests. He maintained business interests on the boards of various railway and shipping companies; for example, he was chairman of the P&O shipping company from 1847 to 1858. He also had an interest in Matheson and Company, the trading agency set up in London in 1848. Matheson followed the well-trodden path of the nineteenth century merchant venturer; make a fortune from some commodity such as sugar or tobacco – usually by exploiting people – retire back home and plough the money into a country pile; build public works such as canals, railways, steamships, museums, libraries and education, thus fueling the juggernaut that was the industrial revolution.

Matheson didn't forget his pals in India. Just a couple of months after he was elected to the House of Commons, he published a book entitled *The Present Position and Prospects of the British Trade with China* which perhaps provided influence for the Indian merchants in their search for compensation. The Spectator magazine reviewed the title: 'we observe that this book, though put together with much art, presents a curious *coup d'oeil* of commercial historical facts and information.' In other words, a triumph of style over substance.

Matheson's first task was to set about helping the people of Ashburton who had been so affected by the disastrous Opium Wars. Matheson's publication showed his approach to bringing about change: action rather than talk. In all his twenty-one years as a Member of Parliament for Ashburton and later for Ross and Cromarty, he never once spoke on the floor of the House of Commons. In Ashburton he stuck to the precedent set by Jardine, ploughing in material aid for the inhabitants and much needed commercial opportunity for the town's mills. The town was in despair and he gave hope and cheer, relieving poverty and suffering.

In July 1843 Matheson purchased the large Ashburton estate of Sir Robert Palk. He proceeded to buy local properties – freeholders and leaseholders – at a good price to put cash into people's hands. It is doubtful that these purchases were made with a view to settling in the area; he had no connection or ties there and there were no prospects. He was immersing himself in the town life of London and the following year would increase his interest in Scotland, adding the Isle of Lewis, which was drawn to his attention by his nephew Alexander Matheson, to his estates, followed two years later by the fishing station of Ullapool, Loch Broom, in Sutherland.

His health was not good at this time and for the next six months he 'paired-off' his parliamentary duties and retired to Leamington Spa for a rest-cure and to take the waters. Meanwhile cash was flowing into the public institutions and mills of Ashburton, keeping the town buoyant. Whilst recovering his health, James Matheson married Mary Jane Percival, on the 9th November 1843, in Edinburgh. He was forty-seven; she was half his age. Her father, Michael Henry Percival, lived in Canada where he was a member of the Legislative Council of Quebec.

By 1844 the people and industries of Ashburton were invigorated and such was the relief of the townsfolk that half of the 4,000 inhabitants subscribed a penny each to purchase an engraved silver snuff-box from a London goldsmith, to be presented as a token of their respect and thanks for his timely patronage. It was a large object an inscription in the centre: 'A tribute of gratitude and respect from the working classes of Ashburton to their representative, friend and benefactor, James Matheson, Esq. M.P. April 1844'.

To underscore this tribute, the inhabitants were determined to have a regular holiday to mark the occasion of the presentation. Matheson was continuing his rest-cure/honeymoon in Italy and it wasn't until January 28th 1845 that his health allowed him and his new wife, along with his soldier brother Thomas, to visit Ashburton and receive the gift. The presentation was lavish, joyous and according to the Western Times correspondent was 'an exhilarating and heart-rejoicing festival in honour of J. Matheson, Esq. M.P. which baffles all language to describe'.

A crowd of three thousand gathered to greet the man and there followed two days of processions, parades, banquets, speeches, fireworks and even a fire-balloon bearing the name Matheson in coloured letters. The townsfolk liked

27

him. John B. Lee, an operational wool comber, was elected to voice a welcome and in eloquent fashion described Matheson's impact on the community: 'Your introduction to us resembled the rising of the sun in all its brilliance after a lengthy stormy night'. Matheson saw the gift as a highly-prized token of the sincere respect and esteem for him of the people of Ashburton.

This calm was, unfortunately, the eye of the storm. As the 1840s progressed, the serge industry slowly collapsed through lack of work. Matheson didn't abandon the town; as late as 1849 he was still giving the Caunter mill orders for serge for the China market as the industry went into terminal decline. Matheson had done his best for the town and its people, but in the words of HJ Hanham: 'He could not save the serge industry, he could only give it a relatively painless burial.'

As early as January 1844, the West Country press had announced Matheson's purchase of the Isle of Lewis 'from the Seaforth family for £190,000 with the intention of spending a further £50,000 or so on establishing a regular steamer service to the island, forming roads and otherwise improving the territory.'

As Matheson moved his interests north – he could do no more for Ashburton – he took many of Ashburton's capable youth into his employment on his Scottish estates. Undoubtedly some Ashburtonians moved to Lewis. 'Tozer', a common surname in Ashburton, was a nickname used in Lewis in the 1920s, for example James Nicolson, a sailor from Knock in Point, and who died in New York, went under that name.

Matheson was only involved with Ashburton for a few years but during that time his impact on the place and the people was all-enveloping and immense. The Liberal Caunter brothers probably developed a good working relationship with Matheson over the years; George the solicitor, John the magistrate, Richard the mill owner and Henry, the 'most capable' of the young Liberals. As the Daily News reported in an 1849 article on the political history of the borough: 'Messrs Matheson and Caunter united are as strong in Ashburton as the firm of Matheson, Jardine and Co. are in China.'

In August of 1845, when James Matheson and his wife first ventured to Lewis, they were given a grand welcoming dinner in Stornoway. One of the few honoured guests at the head of the table was Henry Caunter, who had been given such a warm introduction by Roderick Morrison, the Stornoway banker. 'Henry Caunter' of Ashburton was the toast to which Matheson made the reply. The two men were indeed close and they also shared a passion, a deep interest in science, which was to bring the Industrial Revolution to the heart of the Hebrides.

Chapter Three

James Matheson and Science

James Matheson lived in an age of scientific revolution and was a man with an inquisitive mind. His imagination must have been gripped as the new discoveries were applied to technology. The application of science to practical problems was very appealing to thinking men of commerce. As the historian Allen Andrews has pointed out:

> The Victorians had an honest and unsuspecting admiration for science and saw nothing but good in its developments. The heart of the creed was that science was *useful* and that even the most remotely theoretical discovery would sooner or later be put to material use and benefit in practical life.

According to Richard Grace, as early as 1829 Matheson had tried using the steam powered side-wheeler, Forbes, to improve his trading between India and China but the experiment was not a success. In the late 1820s, the delivery of opium from India to the opium merchants in China needed to be speedier and the vessels more able to combat the monsoon period. One Calcutta agency had tried using the Forbes side-wheeler to tow a sailing ship laden with opium to Canton but suffered a disastrous towing accident. Such was the impression that this new technology left on Matheson that he tried the same ploy with his own sailing craft, the *Jamesina*, but without success – they ran out of coal. No further attempts were made; the crude technology of the time was no match for the fast opium clippers which were sailing the China seas by 1830.

Since the time of Newton in the mid-seventeenth century, the old order of science had developed through small groups of scholars communicating with each other in Latin. By the end of the eighteenth century this progress had given way to a new order as curious minds grasped new experiences and opportunities and discovered new knowledge. The Royal Society, founded in 1667, was still the established authority for recording and directing science and exploration but, with the specialisation of knowledge, fragmentation of the scientific world was occurring. The Geological Society, the Astronomical Society, the Royal Horticultural Society, the Zoological Society of London, the British Association for the Advancement of Science and the Royal Institution were all founded in the first three decades of the nineteenth century to cater for the growing interests of the new generation of specialist, professional men of science.

The Royal Institution was founded in 1799 by Benjamin Thompson, Count Rumford, with the aim of promoting science to help improve life for the lower and middle classes by exploring agricultural chemistry with scientific lectures and laboratory demonstrations. The Royal Institution and the development of local Philosophical Societies and Mechanics Institutes – of which Henry Caunter was a keen supporter – meant that science was no longer the interest solely of scholars, the nobility and aristocracy; the working man was being enlightened.

The end of the eighteenth and the beginning of the nineteenth century was the Romantic Era of science, and Chemistry is often referred to as the signature study of the times. Indeed, the discoveries of chemistry became fashionable; the writer Fievée condemned the inhalation of the newly discovered nitrous oxide or 'laughing gas' as a national vice of the English! In *Chemistry No Mystery*, published by the surgeon John Scoffern in 1839, there is a record of a series of annual lectures in a coastal village in South Devon about the time of Henry Caunter's birth, delivered by an 'Old Philosopher', who demonstrated the preparation and effects of laughing gas. His audience were invited to breathe in the laughing gas with uproarious results:

> some jumped over the tables and chairs; some were bent upon making speeches; some were very much inclined to fight; and one gentleman persisted in attempting to kiss the ladies ... As to the laughing, I think it was chiefly confined to the lookers-on. A few minutes served to restore those maniacs to their senses, and they felt as if nothing had occurred; for it is a peculiarity of this gas that it does not act like intoxicating liquors in producing depression of the spirits, disorder of the stomach, or indeed any other unpleasant effects.

The scene was recorded for posterity by the cartoonist, George Cruikshank, and used as the frontispiece of *Chemistry No Mystery*.

Between 1807 and 1814, during James Matheson's formative years of education, Humphrey Davy discovered eight of the ninety-two classical chemical elements and his *protégé*, Michael Faraday, discovered how to produce electricity mechanically with the dynamo. The latter's experiments of 1831 were said to have 'ended the age of steam and begun the new age of electricity,' although it would be many decades before technology caught up with this assertion.

In astronomy, the siblings William and Caroline Herschell had made huge progress in mapping the night sky and discovering the planet Uranus. The development of geology and of Darwinism allowed a new look at the origins of life which challenged the centuries-old teachings of the Church.

This expansion of science caught the imagination of the artistic and literary minds of the time who were quick to adopt its ideas and language. The Royal Society and the Royal Academy – the guiding body for painting, sculpture and architecture – were both housed in Somerset House in London. The debates on Vitalism and the discovery of electricity influenced Mary Shelley's *Frankenstein*, published in 1817. The poet Samuel Coleridge Taylor keenly attended Humphrey Davy's lectures at the Royal Institution. Following a discussion with the classical scholar William Whewell at the 1830 meeting of the British Association for the Advancement of Science, Coleridge coined the term 'scientist' to describe the new generation of men and women of science whose role was starting to loom large in the minds of the movers and shakers.

In 1824, in Giessen in Germany, the world's first public teaching laboratory for chemistry was opened by Justus von Liebig, a father-figure in the intellectual and practical development of chemistry for years to come. This attracted students from all over Europe and for the next twenty-five years Giessen became the global centre for the teaching of chemistry, producing the cream of the century's chemists and pharmacists. Among them was a certain Benjamin Horatio Paul, a native of Suffolk, who, at the beginning of his long and successful career, was to spend four years developing the Lewis Chemical Works.

This was the *zeitgeist* for an impressionable young mind and it was into this rapidly developing scientific world that James Matheson plunged when he took up residence in London in 1843. That he valued science, maths and knowledge, there is no doubt. At a welcoming banquet in Stornoway in 1845, Regius Professor Gordon of Glasgow University described Matheson's hopes for promoting his newly acquired estate of Lewis:

> What is it that makes a people industrially great? There is but one answer. It is education. That part of education which he [Matheson] was more particularly called upon to inculcate is one of a very special nature; but, viewed generally, is one of vast importance, viz, the application of the doctrines of science in the practical arts.

On the journey home from China, Matheson was presented with a service of silver plate by the merchants of Bombay, as a token of their gratitude for his looking after their interests in the lean times of the Opium Wars. On thanking them, he made reference to the charity of the merchants in their own land, emphasising the importance of education and science: 'When I think of your munificent charity ... the schools and colleges you have funded to diffuse the knowledge and science of the Western world.'

This interest was something that stayed with Matheson. In 1858 when, as Chairman, he presented the prizes at Tain

Academy, he attempted to inspire the young minds before him, exhorting them:

> Next to the study of God's revealed world, that of the mathematician is the most elevatory of all pursuits – the most unerring and surprising in the results to which it conducts us and the most conducive to strengthen and discipline of truth in every department of knowledge. By the aid of mathematics we are enabled to scan the heavens and to ascertain the wonderful laws of the all-wise Creator in maintaining the systems of the Universe. By the aid of mathematics, the sailor traverses the trackless sea as if it were a beaten road and it is a study more or less indispensable in the discovery and perfecting of all the marvellous achievements of modern science in our own day.

Having added a huge fortune to his stock, on his return to Britain Matheson proceeded to add honours. In 1845 he was elected a Fellow of the Royal Geographical Society (RGS), proposed by the Society's Founder and President, Sir Rodney Murchison, and seconded by Bartle Frere and Charles Malcolm. Murchison was a contemporary and fellow-countryman of Matheson, born at Taradale House, Muir of Ord, in 1792. He rose to become one of the most distinguished of geologists, geographers and promoters of science in the early and mid-nineteenth century. How they met is not known but their association prevailed for many years. Murchison was a visitor to Lewis as late as 1860 and enjoyed hunting and shooting breaks with the Mathesons. It was possibly Murchison who brought about the important introduction of minds that was to allow the Lewis Chemical Works to develop in the 1860s. Bartle Frere had become acquainted with Matheson in Bombay where he started as a civil servant, rising to the post of Governor in 1862. John Malcolm had also served time in Bombay as a Rear Admiral of Her Majesty's Indian Navy. Matheson was networking his old contacts well.

Records show that Matheson took no active role in the proceedings of the RGS, but as with his position as an MP, he was a geographical man-of-action rather than a talker – he let his money do that. He indulged his geographical interests with a payment of £1200, via the Treasury, to the Ordnance Survey in order that the Isle of Lewis could jump the queue of all the areas of Scotland awaiting surveying to produce a detailed map. The surveying of Scotland had started in 1819 but was continuing in sporadic fashion. The maps produced were not just of importance to the state; they were an important asset to the nation's landowners as they allowed them an overview of their estates. Legalities, planning developments and improvements with regard to roads, woodlands, farming, draining and mineral exploitation were the markers of the progress of the estate. Matheson could see these advantages and the opportunist was only too keen to sweeten the deal with the Ordnance Survey with an agreement to purchase one hundred copies of the map of Lewis which would be surveyed between 1846 and 1853. In the event, the surveying party of more than one hundred, latterly under the command of Captain Richard Burnaby of the Royal Engineers, took longer than expected. The task was not completed until May 1858, when the Captain was given a grand farewell dinner by the dignitaries and business community of Stornoway in honour of his leadership and conduct in pursuing the task. Matheson knew well how to oil the machinery of Government to achieve his aims and gain advantage. The Ordnance Survey sheet of Lewis was the first to be published of forty-eight sheets mapping Scotland. In March 1859 some 'intelligence' – as news was reported then – appeared in the gossip columns of the Caledonian Mercury:

> Sir James Matheson, the enterprising proprietor of Lewis, being more alive than too many in Scotland to the importance of having an Ordnance Survey of his possessions, made an application to the Ordnance, under the sanction of the Treasury, and, according to the evidence of Mr Hall-Maxwell, secretary of the Highland Society, Sir James was believed to have backed his application by a gift of £1500* to the Government towards the triangulation. At all events, Lewis has got the advantage of an Ordnance Survey which other parts of Scotland may not have for many years to come thanks to the importunity of its proprietor.

Other sources indicate £1200

In June of that same year James Matheson was elected as a Fellow of the Royal Geographical Society. He was also proposed as a Fellow of that august body the Royal Society. Although he had no formal science training (other than a healthy appetite for reading about the subject), as with the Royal Geographical Society, interest, status and wealth were as important a qualification as any formal programme of study. Twenty years before his election, the membership of the Society was composed of about 70% men of science, 20% landed aristocracy and 10% clergy.

With the emergence of the new scientific societies representing the developing disciplines of science – geology, zoology, horticulture, astronomy etc – the Royal Society itself was rapidly changing away from being a 'club'. Again it was his pal Sir Rodney Murchison who, on 27th June

1845, proposed James Matheson as a Fellow. In his memoirs Murchison describes how in the late 1830s and not long before Matheson's election: 'Any wealthy or well-known person, any MP or bank-director or East Indian nabob who wished to have FRS added to his name was sure to obtain admittance by canvassing and by being elected at any ordinary meeting'.

To secure his Fellowship, a further twelve Fellows seconded Matheson, some of whom were probably acquaintances from his days out east; Sir George Staunton headed the Honourable East India Company's factory in Canton and John Crawford was the East India Company's administrator in India and Singapore. His other proposers were a mix of eminent physicians, bankers, a judge and a poet. The net-working was continuing.

On 19th Jan 1846 James Matheson was duly elected as a Fellow of the Royal Society. His citation, 'Attached to science and anxious to promote its progress' seems to sum up his subsequent actions in the following years, with respect to exploiting the natural resources of his recently acquired Isle of Lewis. As with the RGS, he was never active within the business of the Royal Society, except to second applications for Fellowship.

He was now James Matheson FRS, FRGS. If only he had taken note of the motto of the Royal Society, *Nullius in Verba* (take nobody's word for it), and heeded the sentiment, the exploitation and development of Lewis may well have taken a different course.

Chapter Four

To Lewis

'*Failte don nachdaran do dh'Eilais as Fheidh s'do dh'oirthir an Eisg*'
(Welcome to the Proprietor to the Island of
Red Deer and Salmon)
A banner of welcome to the Mathesons

On the 29th August 1845, an interesting report appeared in the columns of the John O'Groat Journal:

> Mr Matheson, proprietor of the island of Lewis, arrived at Stornoway on the 15th current, by the 'Falcon' steamer and was received by the inhabitants of the island with every demonstration of attachment which their remote position and circumstances enabled them to command. Flags were flying from vessels, boats and houses. About three-o-clock p.m. the steamer rounded the point of Holm and entered the harbour with flying colours and soon after Mr Matheson landed under a salute

from the shore conducted by Mr MacKenzie, town clerk, amid the enthusiastic acclamation of the people. In the evening bonfires were lighted on the surrounding hills which had a splendid appearance; there was also a brilliant display of fireworks on the hill above Lewis Lodge conducted by Mr John MacLeod.

There then followed a reception for Mr and Mrs Matheson, given in the Masonic Hall by the townspeople, with speeches, toasts, merriment and song. 'There has been no occurrence in the island for many years which has awakened such an interest as Mr Matheson's visit,' concluded the Journal's correspondent. Stornoway was stirred.

Matheson must have felt that the public fêting that he had received on his triumphant reception in Ashburton in January had followed him to the other end of the country. It would have given him encouragement, if any were needed, at the start of his involvement with another community. But things would be different.

For a while the island had suffered from neglect. The previous landlord – James Stewart Mackenzie – had been absent fulfilling his duties as Governor of the Ionian Islands and subsequently, Ceylon (Sri Lanka), leaving the management of the island in the hands of trustees in Edinburgh. This resulted in little money for maintenance, continued improvements or benefits for the tenants.

The people had also suffered a loss of income from various sources. The manufacture of kelp from seaweed had declined now that new, cheap sources of soda were available, manufactured on an industrial scale from salt using the Leblanc process. Kelp burning was not altogether extinguished; in 1851 kelp ash was still being produced in Lochs, south of Stornoway, and exported to Glasgow, and the people of Balallan were paying their rents from the proceeds of kelp production. The illegal distillation of whisky using locally-grown barley had been stopped and replaced by landlord-owned legal distilleries in Stornoway (1825) and Ness (1831). The Stornoway distillery, which was on the site of the present-day Woodland Centre in the Lews Castle Grounds, was known as the Shoe Burn distillery and built at a cost of £14,000. It was recorded in the New Statistical Account in 1833 as being:

> on a grand scale with coppers of large diameter, furnaces, vats, coolers ... a very large malt barn and mill. The whole process and apparatus are constructed upon the most improved plans ... no expense has been spared by the proprietor to make it complete; but it is not yet in operation.

The falling price of cattle added to the people's woes; the times were not kind to the crofters outwith the town. The Rev Mr Norman MacLeod raised public funds to relieve the years of destitution that were 1836 and 1837. The New Statistical Account boldly stated: 'The island of Lewis is a full century behind other parts of Scotland in agriculture and domestic improvement – the town and inhabitants of Stornoway and a few tacksmen accepted.'

So the crofting community of Lewis was in a depressed state when Matheson arrived and the principal complaint was high rent and short leases. There was much for him to address. The Inverness Journal of 19th January 1845 was enthusiastically banging the drum for Lewis when it announce the purchase of the island: 'The fisheries may be rendered highly productive and in the interior of the country there is ample scope for cultivation, planting and draining which will furnish employment to the poor inhabitants and be the means of improving their social and moral improvement.'

Having spent £190,000 on the purchase of Lewis, Matheson proceeded to spend as much again to try to bring about change as he had done in Ashburton. In that borough he was the people's representative in the House of Commons – a post he didn't relinquish until the General Election of 1847 when he was elected as MP for Ross and Cromarty (his brother Lt. Col. Thomas Matheson replaced him in Ashburton). As an MP in Ashburton, Matheson acted for the people and was seen as a man of action, a man of power and influence. He had helped, directly, local merchants to run their well-established businesses with orders and he helped the families of the local community, employed by the mills, with money and in-kind. In Lewis, by contrast, he was the landowner, a man of absolute power and all that that encompassed. He would discover that delegating power as a landlord was not the same as delegating power in commerce, which had been his life's experience.

When Matheson purchased Lewis, did he know what he was buying? Did he seek any advice as to what needed developed or improved or to be wary of? There appears to be no record of Matheson commissioning a survey of the island – other than the 'commissioned' Ordnance Survey – unlike a previous owner, Lord Seaforth, the father-in-law of James Stewart Mackenzie. In 1800, Lord Seaforth received a survey of the island, together with a number of suggestions as to how the mineral wealth of Lewis could be exploited and the lives of the crofters improved. This was the work of Rev Mr James Headrick of Edinburgh, a natural science enthusiast who had studied agriculture and mineralogy across Great Britain: many large estates had been planned by him and improved under his direction.

Headrick experimented on his observations made in Lewis and had plenty of advice for the crofters as well as the proprietor. As far as developments were concerned, he included the more general use of liming using shell sand from the beaches to sweeten the acidic peaty soils; the burning of limestone – found in Garrabost – to provide the local building trade with lime; a thorough investigation of the extraction of iron from the abundant deposits of iron ore using sulphur-free black peat; salt manufacture; glass-making and, in particular, the development of the Garrabost and Ness clay deposits into an island industry: 'Towards the village of Garrabost the clay contains no lime, though blue, it is rusty, is endowed with great tenacity and is well-adapted for making bricks, tiles and several species of coarser earthenware.'

> As an important resource for this potential industry he includes the people of Lewis who: 'discover a surprising skill in making a sort of earthenware vessels which they call crugies. The solidity and neatness with which they make these vessels astonished me considering they have no tools to work with but their hands alone. But the skills they have acquired in these matters affords a basis on which a flourishing manufacture may be reared.'

The New Statistical Account, written some thirty years later, gives a good description of the pottery manufacture, the pots being referred to as 'craggans':

> The red clay is kneaded as smooth as glazier's putty, the vessel is fashioned by one hand inside, the other on the outside, till it is brought to the size and shape required. After hardening in the sun for a time, a peat fire is kindled around it, till it becomes red. Warm milk is then poured into it. This gives it a polish and a gloss. If it does not crack, it is considered as a good dish, and the boiled milk is drunk by the potters.

Headrick doesn't mention peat in his report, other than stressing the importance of correctly replacing turf, but he did carry out experiments on the distillation of seaweed to produce varnish and oil and to which he attaches great promise. As for improvements, he suggests that the principal business of the island should be fisheries, with good quays and harbours (including a jetty to Goat Island to create a large eastern basin): 'But what would crown the prosperity of Stornoway and contribute highly to the improvement of the Isle of Lewis would be the construction of a proper quay to which vessels of all magnitudes might lay their sides.'

He backed this up with other ideas: developing open-sea herring fishing with larger vessels; placing buoys on rocks to mark safe access; and regular on-shore markets with fresh produce to victual boats which would attract vessels on passage and create revenue.

On land Headrick was keen to promote plantations and reclamation and drainage to create good, sweet pasture; to increase livestock was seen as essential. He railed noisily against the lazy-bed system, advocating a more efficient husbandry using broad strips of land. At a practical level, the road system had to be improved and he describes the main arteries of present-day Lewis. On a human level, he suggests that in order to bring about these improvements, crofters should be granted at least a nineteen year lease.

The report contains a lot of advice which Lord Seaforth and later his son-in-law James Stewart MacKenzie put into practice. Lord Seaforth was interested in the fishing and kelp industries and completed four miles of road-making in six years. James Stewart MacKenzie introduced drift-net fishing for herring in the Minch and built cod smacks to take live cod directly to London in a sea-water well built into the hull of the boat. He drained ground between

Stornoway and Mossend to create arable ground; improved and created new roads and set up schools for the learning of spinning and weaving. Crofters were encouraged to grow flax to provide the linen required.

Although written well before the arrival of Matheson, Matheson undoubtedly read the document. It was freely published in 1816 and at a later date Matheson donated a copy to the Literary Association of Stornoway. Headrick's observational and experimental scientific approach would have appealed to Matheson. The fact that he responded immediately to some of the suggestions – clay bricks and tiles, roads, drainage, liming – could have been a direct result of Headrick's report.

So, Matheson, the man of action, set to and in the words of the Royal Society Proceedings 'with large hearted and liberal plans he entered on his self-imposed task, employing the most able assistants whom he could find to carry out his projects.'

On 27th August, a fortnight after arriving on Lewis, Matheson and his wife were given an honorary dinner in the Masonic Hall by the respected dignitaries of the town; another grand affair with the town's officials, professionals, merchants, clergy and men of commerce and of the sea, all eager to meet their new landlord. As befitted the occasion there was dining, toasts, speeches, music, singing and much merriment. The hall was decorated with the Matheson coat-of-arms and with a banner bearing the greeting, '*Failte don nachdaran do dh'Eilais as Fheidh s'do dh'oirthir an Eisg.*' (Welcome to the Proprietor to the Island of Red Deer and Salmon.)

The people knew where their wealth lay. Sitting next to James at the top table were the Chairman, Roderick Morrison the banker, Henry Caunter and William Smith from Deanston. In a report of his speech, Matheson gave the assembled throng hope and confidence for good things to come with a forthright and pragmatic assertion of his intentions:

> I am well aware how vain will be all my endeavours to increase the resources of the island and better the condition of the inhabitants without your assistance and cooperation; but from what I have already seen, and more particularly from what I now witness, I feel confident that in this respect, nothing will be wanting on your part. I cannot conceal from myself that the task I have undertaken is arduous – one of great difficulty.

As to the how, Matheson continued; 'I made up my mind to engage a Highland factor, and employ Highlanders on all occasions where practicable. I am anxious that the main improvements should rest with our own people and that the executive should be in their hands.'

Regarding the hinterland of Lewis: 'Our task in the interior will be more difficult but with time and perseverance I can see no cause to despair. It is my opinion, and that of Mr Scobie [factor] that much good may be affected by inducing the small tenants to improve the land on their own account and it is our intention to give them every encouragement and necessary assistance.'

A week later, in that 1845 autumn of promise, the Masonic Hall once more resounded to merriment until the early hours of the morning as the Mathesons, in return, hosted a Grand Ball for their visitors and the Town. This time the banner read 'Measgaich subhachas le gliòcus' (Mirth tempered with Wisdom), the Matheson motto, and the hall and revellers glittered as they 'formed a scene which could scarcely have been anticipated in so remote a locality, and one which called forth the repeated admiration of several distinguished visitors – particularly while the far-famed polka was danced in all its perfection.'

In reality Matheson was to depart from his noble intentions, as the formation of farms and the exploitation of clay and peat took precedence, rather than the development of the fisheries and the granting of leases. As W Anderson Smith was to reflect, in his tales of Lewis some thirty years later: 'Accustomed to the imperious manner of the East and the exact methods of commercial life, Mr Matheson entered upon a charge that demanded a very different tone of mind to be approached with success.'

In contrast to his dealings in Ashburton, Matheson didn't use local talent. He brought in an estate manager, John Scobie from Sutherland, to be his factor, to control the running of the estate and to oversee his many projects and improvements. In 1846 a start was made on building the Tudor-style Lews Castle overlooking Stornoway. It took about three years to complete and was a grand affair. It has recently been restored, extended and given a new lease of life. It was built using local stone and brick although the white sandstone came from Glasgow and the granite for the octagonal tower, from Colonsay. The building contractor was Peter MacNab from Oban and much of the labour came from the Oban area; 'strangers' as they were known. One notable Stornoway stonemason who worked on the gargoyles and staircase balustrade was the father of Donald Morison whose manuscript provides much of the history of the Lewis Chemical Works. The building of the castle involved the clearing of villages and good grazing land to establish the parklands. The provision of employment to local people in that part of the construction and in drainage and trenching would be of little compensation to those removed from their houses and land.

William Smith, from Deanston in Perthshire, an agriculturalist with a reputation, arrived in 1845 to revolutionise land-husbandry using scientific methods. He had been described by Professor Gordon in that welcoming speech to Matheson as 'a most able and successful promulgator of the doctrines of Liebig.'

Liebig had recently discovered the importance of proper plant nutrition. Smith had brought 2000 acres of previously unworked moorland, possibly in the Highlands, into productive use which was let out to tenants for growing crops. In Lewis, Smith deliberately chose an area of ground of poor quality, near Lochganvich in the centre of the island, such was his belief that his methods would succeed and demonstrate the extent of the possibilities for the island. A small community of eight houses, also named Deanston, eventually developed and the project initially showed promise, producing thriving root and grain crops. In 1848, the Scottish Farmer reported that 'finer oats, potatoes and turnips could not be desired.'

John Scobie said of William Smith at a public dinner given for his services: 'We now have only to look across to this neighbourhood to see the heavy crops of turnips on the new drained land. The tussac grass is also flourishing here and the Timothy grass is the wonder of all who visit the islands.'

Sadly, after just four years, all the dyke building, draining, ditching and fertilising which had provided much needed labour, was deemed a failure and the experiment abandoned.

In Stornoway, new houses and a water works were built and a gas works established to light the streets of the town. A gaol and an industrial school added to the amenities and the harbour was greatly improved, with the building of new walls and the installation of a patent slip for the building and refitting of boats. A market place was constructed for the sale of butcher's meat and fresh vegetables to shipping as Headrick's blue-print for Lewis came to life. Matheson had plans to replace the Shoe Burn Distillery with a purpose built building near Laxdale: he objected to the close proximity of the operation to his Castle.

The steamer service to the mainland was poor and in 1846 Matheson started a regular weekly service to the island, between Stornoway and Glasgow, using the *Mary Jane*, a vessel he commissioned on the Clyde and named after his new bride.

As Matheson was establishing his tenure of the island, tragedy struck the Hebrides. A failure of the potato crop in 1845 as a result of disease coincided with a poor grain harvest and depressed cattle prices, once again reducing the crofting community to a state of destitution. Matheson, the man-of-action, immediately supplied meal to his tenants – albeit at a 75% discount and in exchange for labour on his various schemes; trenching, draining, road-making and repairing, building dykes, bridges and quays and planting tussac grass, a hardy species of grass native to the Falkland islands. All this didn't go unnoticed as the John O'Groat Journal reported on the 10th January 1851: 'The Queen has conferred the dignity of Baronet of the United Kingdom on James Matheson, Esq, of Achany and the Lewis, FRS, on account of his distinguished merits and noble assistance which he gave to the inhabitants of Lewis in a year of famine.'

In 1845, John Scobie, Matheson's factor, departed and was succeeded by John Munro Mackenzie. He was a native Lewisman, a trained engineer working on the Caledonian Railway with plenty of managerial experience and who understood land improvement. He was a man of sensitivity, sympathetic to the crofters' way of life; a hard life as described by the Rev Mr MacRae of Barvas: 'Their whole round of duty consists in securing fuel, in sowing and reaping the scanty crops, and in rearing their flocks and in tending them at pasture.'

Like John Scobie, John Munro Mackenzie earned a reputation of being firm, fair and honest in his dealings with the crofters and fishermen. In 1851 he kept a diary for a year which gives a clear, intimate, objective picture of the stresses and strains of island life for all at that time. He knew that the way to alleviate the economic problems of the island was the active development of the fishing industry, especially deep-sea fishing, but Matheson chose to think otherwise. He believed that it was those who stood to make money out of the trade – the fish curers and fishermen – who should build the harbours. In 1847 Matheson had purchased the fishing station of Ullapool, on Loch Broom on the eastern shores of the Minch, for £5,000 from the British Fishing Society. The port had been in decline for a number of years as a result of the departure of the herring from the loch, the shoals moving as the climate and the ocean slowly changed. Perhaps Matheson saw fishing as an unreliable investment, outwith his control and too much at the caprice of nature.

Sir James heeded Headrick's advice as he set about exploiting the mineral wealth of the island by establishing a brick and tile works at Garrabost, to use the abundant supply of clay. The brick works were to become an important feature in the operation of the Lewis Chemical Works but were a substantial manufactory in their own right, providing employment and income for the Garrabost area. According to the Ordnance Survey Name Book of 1848, the foreman of the works was a Mr S Philips and '[the Brick Works] were commenced on 1st March 1847 and carried on by Mr Mathieson [sic], the proprietor. There are two workmen employed on the establishment who make at the rate of 3,000 bricks per day each or 36,000 weekly. There is a steam engine of 15 horse power being fitted up.'

This sounds like a super-human effort but this rate of production for pressed bricks was normal working practice for a twelve – fourteen hour day, although the potential output was probably never realised. In 1851, four years after the brickworks had started, John Munro MacKenzie, recorded in his diary: 'Went to Garrabost and inspected the tile works which is now doing well and turning out a large quantity of tiles, the weather being favourable and the work in good order ... settled with the work people at the Brick works retaining the greater part of their wages for rent.'

All was not rosy at Garrabost! Over the summer, doubts surfaced concerning the brickworks. Matheson's improvements had stopped and production appeared to be sporadic, with the viability of the works being in question. On 30th May 1851 MacKenzie writes:

> Proceeded to Garrabost and remained there all day paying workmen and taking inventory of tools, iron and other articles at the Tile works, discharged several of the work people and gave others notice that their services would not be required after next month. As the drainage works are now about being completed and no demand for bricks or tiles, I fear these works must be thrown idle on account of the great expense of cartage to and from the works and the high price which must be paid for the coals, with other causes tiles cannot be made here so cheap as further south and if they have to be exported there will be additional charge for the freight.

MacKenzie was no fan of manufacturing on Lewis and this was an early indication to Matheson – if he was ever made aware of it – that a manufactory on Lewis was bound to entail extra costs due to its remote location and the need to transport raw materials in and products out of the island. Over the summer the foreman of the works was retained and by September the people of Garrabost were once again benefiting from the exploitation of the clay. MacKenzie's gloomy outlook seems to have passed: 'Rents of Township [Garrabost] pretty well paid up, principally on account of the employment given at the Brick and Tile Works.'

The bricks, roof and drain tiles produced at Garrabost were used throughout the island until the works closed sometime in the 1880s. Two types of brick were produced: rough bricks of slightly irregular size, smaller than a modern brick; and a larger, uniform, smooth brick, stamped 'Lews Brick'. One of the first structures built using Lews bricks – just five months after the Brick Works started – was the Water Works, situated on the top of Ranol Hill, in the middle of the present day Stornoway golf course. The row of four tanks – each about twenty-five feet square and fifteen feet deep – would have required thousands of the bricks. Fifteen months after the building of these works started, Captain Burnaby, the OS surveyor, reported that the works were still to be completed.

Laxdale and Leurbost schools were built using the brick as was the Imperial Hotel, latterly used as the Louise Carnegie hostel, which stood on South Beach Street in Stornoway. It was demolished about 1991 and the bricks used to make the foundation of the present-day An Lanntair arts centre. It wasn't just utility buildings that were constructed from the bricks; Ardvourlie Castle in north Harris and Lews Castle in Stornoway both have internal walls constructed from the red Lews brick. The clay drainage tiles, naturally, were buried, but a drain outfall can be seen in the banking of the main drive approaching Cuddy Point in the grounds of Lews Castle.

By 1851, the situation on Lewis was starting to improve as the herring fishery in Caithness developed, giving islanders a new source of income if they were willing to travel. Matheson encouraged this, giving free passage to the mainland for those willing to go. He also gave free mussel bait to Banff fishermen when west coast proprietors were unwilling to sell their own mussels. Matheson was quite willing to help fishing if it cost him next to nothing.

In that year the improvement plans were stopped. Although he had undoubtedly ploughed a lot of money into Lewis, it did not necessarily go in the right direction to secure the future for his tenants who were, by this time, being encouraged to emigrate. As Donald MacDonald points out in his book, *Lewis*: 'Of the £99,720 spent on the building of houses and land reclamation, nothing was spent on the housing of the crofters, as was all too evident, and up to 1853, only £8,471 was spent on their lands with a further £3,000 later on. All of this was eventually repaid [in rent].'

In 1853, John Munro MacKenzie left Lewis for Cumberland and was replaced by Donald Munro, a solicitor originally from Tain, who had come to Lewis in 1841. Unlike his predecessors, Donald Munro was to be a blight on the Lewis landscape, as the feudal autonomy of the management system allowed him, over the next twenty-five years, to earn the odium of the crofters for his mean, bullying, hateful and desperate actions; behaviour which reflected badly on Sir James Matheson and made the people wary of their landlord, despite his decisive action when the destitution had descended on them.

It would be a while before Matheson's inclinations towards firing the furnaces of industrial chemistry took root but the fireworks ignited on the Mathesons' arrival would not be repeated when they departed, by which time the crofters must have felt that, in the words of W. Anderson Smith, James Matheson had not only purchased the island but its population as well.

PART TWO

Peat, Politics and People

Chapter One

The Lewis Peatlands

'... a huge inanimate chaos.'
Dr BH Paul

By the time Dr Benjamin Paul left Lewis in 1862, after four years spent developing the Lewis Chemical Works, island life had left quite an impression on him. He saw the peat moors as very much a barrier to the development of a sustained way of life for the inhabitants:

> The peat deposits of these islands, though containing the elements of social amelioration, of industry and of wealth, lie like a huge inanimate chaos, burying the land which might yield abundant harvests, preventing the labour of the inhabitants and the development and maturing of crops in those few patches of ground that are yet cultivated.

Although Paul's work at the Lewis Chemical Works did show the industrial potential of peat, the people of Lewis had long since learned to harvest the moorland, living in rhythm with the island's topography. Cutting peat for fuel and creating lazy-beds for the cultivation of crops allowed them to sustain a simple way of life.

How had this 'inanimate chaos' developed on Lewis in contrast to the loamy soils of much of Britain? 500 years ago, whilst travelling around Wales, the antiquarian John Leland developed the idea that lack of critical grazing by cattle and sheep had allowed the peat to develop. Imagination created other theories: peat had been deposited from the sea as the wreck of a floating island; peat was actually alive – a growing organism. With time, more rational theories produced current thinking. The peat on Lewis started to form about 3,000 years ago as the climate changed and cool, wet weather prevailed. The waterlogged conditions in the ground, kept cool by the constant surface evaporation by the wind, resulted in a shortage of oxygen which prevented bacteria and fungi from growing. This in turn prevented the decay of plant material by these micro-organisms to form humus. As acid conditions developed, helped by the underlying rocks, acid loving sphagnum mosses and heathers, along with sun-dew and bog-cotton, thrived. When they died, their remains became buried and compressed under the weight of subsequent layers of plant growth and, slowly, chemistry did its work, converting the plant remains – litter – into peat.

The clean face of a freshly cut peat bank reveals these slow, centuries-long chemical reactions that have occurred underground. As the reactions change the plants into peat, the boundless energy of the sun, taken up by the living plant, is stored in the peat, to be released when the fuel is burned.

The character of the peat ranges from the stringy, light, spongy, brown form, found just below the turf, to the black, dense, hard, coal-like fuel found sitting on the bedrock; the result of continued chemical reaction and better at giving out heat when burned. Depending on location and condition, it is reckoned that peat accumulates at a considerable rate, as fast as one foot every fifty to a hundred years. On Lewis the peat can reach a depth of sixteen feet, but on average the covering is about five feet deep. In 1857, James Matheson had the Callanish standing stones cleared of peat at the suggestion of his friend Henry Caunter, who, amongst his many talents numbered that of antiquarian. The 5,000 year old stones were covered with a layer of peat which had accumulated since the peat had started to form 3,000 years earlier. In a letter to the Society of Antiquaries of Scotland, Matheson described the scene of the excavation: 'The average depth of the moss from the surface to a rough causewayed basement in which the circle stones were embedded was five feet.'

At a glance, the unwelcoming, hostile environment of the Lewis peat moorland would seemingly prevent people from surviving, let alone thriving. On an island mostly devoid of any trees, peat is the only readily available fuel, so ironically, the presence of peat was very much the bottom line for survival. The loss of a good source of peat or of the peat stack itself was a serious threat. The Great Storm and high tide of 29th January 1869 swept away all the peat stacks from fifty houses at Newton in Stornoway, leaving the poor inhabitants vulnerable with no winter fuel. One of the reasons for the island of Mingulay being abandoned in 1911 was the lack of peat and in 1879 the crofters of Bosta, in the island of Bernera, asked to be removed to Kirkibost as their peat moor was running out.

This strong connection between the crofter and his source of fuel was turned to their advantage by Matheson's factors; unless rents were paid on time, no peats could be cut. John Munro MacKenzie, the second of Matheson's factors, describes in his diary how the Ness fishermen arranged for the fish curers to vouch for their rents:

> 23rd May 1851. Great numbers of the Ness Fishermen have come to town and are calling at the office with letters from the Curers becoming bound for the payment of their rents, as I prevented their cutting peats 'till they have either paid their rents or given satisfactory Security, this rule applies to all who were served with notices of removal over the whole estate but it will be difficult to carry it out, tho' already many are coming forward to give security.

The results indicate that for the people, MacKenzie's word as factor was enough; his threat did not need to include abuse as was the way of his successor, Donald Munro.

The peat fire did not just heat the home. Generally left smouldering, the peat was set to burning when heat was required for cooking and not just to boil the pot or heat the griddle. W. Anderson Smith describes, in his book *Lewisiana*, how, in 1874, the Lewis crofter was able to use smouldering peat ash, which burns for hours, to bake bread. The recipe was simple; seawater, soured flour for yeast, and fresh flour: 'Mix thoroughly, drop into the well-greased pot, and when it has risen, sink deep into the hot peat ashes. Cut and come again.'

The peat reek, the strong eye-watering smoke from the burning peat, was an important element, pervading the crofters' lives. This smoke was an essential ingredient in the making of manure for feeding the crops and conditioning the heavy soil. In 1875, William Blake wrote in Harpers New Monthly Magazine about his tour of Lewis, describing the construction of the houses:

The absence of a chimney is considered a necessity. The hut consists of a thick wall of un-mortared stone and turf rising about six feet from the ground. The roof is constructed to spars of wood which serve as rafters and these are thickly covered with masses of straw, which again has an upper covering of slices of turf. Inside a peat fire is always burning – or rather when it is not being used for cooking, smouldering – and the hut is almost always filled with a thick, pungent, yet fragrant smoke, strong enough to make the eyes start of a stranger who enters into the dusky dwelling. Now it is the object of the occupiers of these hovels to prevent by every means the escape of smoke which, from day to day, goes on slowly saturating the straw of the roof until it is as black as the peat itself. This saturated straw forms an excellent manure.

When peat burns, ammonia is released which would render the straw particularly effective as a manure. W. Anderson Smith also made observations about the peat reek tickling not only his sense of smell but also his taste buds:

On top of the thatched dwelling, the colony of fowls finds warmth and a congenial roost. This artificial heat is said to make them lay much more readily than they would otherwise do. It supplies them with a sort of tropical climate at all seasons for the peat fire is never extinguished or allowed to lapse night or day. At the same time there is the drawback of having their eggs always impregnated with a subtle flavour of peat smoke, which to some palates is an insurmountable obstacle to their enjoyment.

The all-pervading peat reek not only nourished the land and seasoned the produce but it also saved lives. In 1860 Dr Millar, the only doctor in Lewis at the time, was impressed by the immunity of the islanders to TB. Dr G Clark, who practiced in Harris, had very few TB patients in thirty-two years of practice. The consensus amongst medical men was that the antiseptic properties of peat smoke killed off the tuberculosis bacterium. Charles MacRae practiced as a doctor in Stornoway for well over fifty years and into the twentieth century. In 1848, whilst studying under Sir James Simpson – he who discovered the anaesthetic chloroform – MacRae won a gold medal for his thesis on 'The Antiseptic Properties of Peat Smoke'. As W. Anderson Smith observed in 1874:

> It is an unquestionable fact, vouched for by the medical practitioners long settled in the country [Lewis], that tubercular consumption is seldom or never found among the natives who have always remained in Lewis. Natives who have been away for a time, especially girls in service, not seldom return smitten unto death. So, it cannot be said to be the native constitution so much as the condition of their existence that we must look for explanation. The quantity of fish oil and marine products devoured may have a beneficial influence, but above and before all, our conviction is that we must look at the healthy effect of the blessed peat reek, with which, during half their existence, their lungs are impregnated. Whenever they leave the health-giving outer atmosphere it is to enter into a strongly antiseptic one.

Peat reek sometimes provided balm of a different sort. Living on an island, people learned to adapt when inevitable shortages of various commodities occurred. Murdo Morrison of Bragar and Wishaw, relates how peat was smoked in times of want: 'As a very unpleasant alternative there was calcas, a fibrous material found on some peats. It was hot and utterly vile but it was there when cigarettes were not.'

The traditional way of smoking tobacco or its peat substitute was to recycle an unbroken shell of a lobster claw as a pipe, described by the Point poet William MacKenzie in his reflections from Canada on Lewis life; 'Chan 'Eil Duil Agam Tilleadh' ('I don't expect to return'):

> 'Se 'n giomach bha gòrach thug bloigh dhuit
> dha òrdaig
> Gu smogaigeadh còsadh cruach mhòine Neill Shaoir.'
> ('The lobster was foolish to give you half of his claw
> To smoke the dross of Neill Saoir's peat stack.')

The lobster pipe even found its way into smoking history as an exhibit in the Wills Tobacco Company Museum in Bristol.

The cutting of peat was a major event in the crofting calendar; it was essential and had to be carried out. Despite the apparent physical work involved, the task was approached with a light heart, according to the New Statistical Account: 'The peat cutting season is one of joy and hilarity. Eggs, butter, cheese and whisky are brought to the peat bank.'

The first task in April or May was to turf the bank, by removing the top foot of turf – a spade's depth – to reveal the underlying peat. Dr Benjamin Paul, the Lewis Chemical Works chemist, described the opening up of a new peat bank:

> After removing the surface sods at the places
> where the trenches are to be cut, for a width

of three feet along the whole line of the trench, the peat cutter digs out the peat with a peculiar shaped tool, in slices of about a foot square and three or four inches thick. As fast as these slices are cut another man takes them off the peat iron and throws them on the surface so as to spread them out as much as possible and the number of slices cut is just as many as a man can throw on both sides of the trench without shifting his position except from one end to the other as the cutter advances.

The opening of the trench created two peat banks, one on each side, which were cut in subsequent years. The next task was for the women to lift the peats and place them on edge, leaning against each other in small piles of three or four, called *rudhans* [pronounced roo-ans]. The drying of the surface of the peat is an irreversible process and the drying peat can stand rain showers without wetting as Paul describes:

When mountain peat is spread out on the ground during dry weather, the drying goes on rapidly, the surface of the pieces acquire a kind of skin which is not wetted again by rain, and the peat in the course of a week, is sufficiently hardened to be handled; the pieces are then set up on edge so that the air may play on both sides and in the course of six weeks or two months they are dry enough to be stacked or heaped up.

The peat iron, or *tarasgair* [pronounced tarasker], was a type of two bladed spade. The design varied throughout the peat cutting areas of Britain and Ireland – the Highlands, the Scottish Borders, Northumbria, Wales, Somerset and Dartmoor among others. The design often reflected the way in which the job was done and whether it was a two-man or one-man operation. On Lewis, the iron consisted of a narrow steel spade, about three inches by one foot with a five foot wooden handle wedged into the back. The handle had a foot-step attached just above the blade, to aid pushing the iron into the peat. Attached at right angles to the base of the spade was a second blade about two and a half inches deep and a foot long and sharpened at its lower edge in order to slice the peat off the bank. The peat was therefore cut away on two sides and detached at its base by a backward pull of the handle, once the blade had been pushed down to the required depth.

After a couple of weeks, depending on the weather, the women would take over to help the drying of the peat and the men would be away to the fishing. Marriages were made on this essential division of labour, as W. Anderson Smith noted:

> But before a Lews young man can hope to make a good matrimonial bargain, he must go to the Wick fishing. Once he has proved his manhood by bringing back a few pounds from the everlasting Northern harvest, he can calmly look around for the girl that can carry the biggest creel of peats across the moor, or the heaviest creel of seaweed from the beach. Let him add to this a scrap of a lot from the laird, or from his father, and as soon as he has knocked up a hut, he is a remarkably marriageable young man.

The peats were gathered into larger piles as drying proceeded. They were then taken by creel across the moor to the nearest track for transporting by pony and cart, the women knitting while carrying the vast, bulky loads on their backs. The stack of peat would be built out on the moor as a small conical structure or near to the house where a large carefully crafted peat stack was made. The stack had to be built in such a way that it would not fall down and so that it would shed water and keep the centre of the stack dry. Flat peats were used to build the rectangular wall; angled on edge leaning against each other in rows producing a herringbone structure. The peats were piled inside this wall – one end of the wall being left open – with turfs on top to keep out rain. The stack was a work of skill and knowledge. It was usual to cut a year in advance; if the weather was poor there was still fuel for the coming year, although the peat would weather with time and lose some of its vigour. As W. Anderson Smith relates: 'A crofter will cut enough in a day or two to last him the year through, but peats require to be well dried in the sun, and, as this depends on the summer, most crofters take care to have a good supply in advance for fear of a wet year.'

Until about thirty years ago, peat cutting was still a widespread communal activity; the only changes being the replacement of the creel, pony and cart with a tractor and trailer. Jessie Leary of Garrabost recalls peat cutting in the 1930s when the activity hadn't changed for centuries:

> You went out and turfed your peat bank, then when it came to cutting you had to drop the turf in line to the peat bank, inside it; it all fell into place if you started at the right end, and of course that eventually went down into the ground again. Then it [the exposed surface of peat] was cleaned and you started to cut it. On this side of the island they have peat banks that

are four or five peats deep, whereas, on other parts of the island they are lucky if they have two deep. In the old days they used to have crews; everybody would come round to your house and cut the peats with you, and you in turn would cut their peats with them. You'd need eight of you at least and they'd come to the house first of all and they'd have what they called a 'little breakfast' – a boiled egg and a cup of tea – and they headed off. They'd come back at 10 am and have a proper breakfast – porridge, bacon and egg – and off they'd go to the peats again. They spent an awful lot of time walking backwards and forwards. And then they'd come home for their dinner; they might get soup and meat or herring and potatoes, but there was always a pudding, and off they'd go again. Around 4 or 5pm, somebody would go out to the peat bank loaded with cakes and sandwiches and tea which they'd have out at the peat bank and that was the working day.

And then came the lifting. Everybody did their own lifting unless you went and helped someone and they'd come and help you. There was no tractors in those days so you had to carry them on your back [in a creel] to the road. You'd throw a peat to one side in a certain place and you'd count how many peats was there and you could reckon if you needed two carts or if you needed one cart – keep a tally. We used to have two carts and they used to reckon about 15 creels to a cart, stacked high to a point, everybody trying to outdo each other how much they put [in the creel]! Oh, no wonder they died young then, God help us. They'd stack it up neatly. There was one man in the village, Don MacKay, he was very strict on them with the cart. He had a lovely little horse called Ginger, a dainty little thing. His cart had to be perfect. A woman would be standing on each wheel and he would be standing on the arms of the cart and they'd stack the peat 'till they got it nice and neat so none would fall. But heaven help them if any of it fell off his cart, he'd be telling them off. And then there'd be two or three at the peat stack setting up the stack while the carts were to-ing and fro-ing and there'd be just a banter going on and you'd have a sigh of relief the day it was all over. It was a pleasure sometimes just to be out in the nice fresh air and it was a great night afterwards. When you finished the peats you'd come in and have a cup of tea, a dram, and maybe a sing song and a real chat.

Also in the 1930s, a young John 'Tonkan' MacDonald of Flesherin, Point, used to go to the peats, carried in the creel on his mother's back:

I used to love that – you had a great view over her shoulder. On her way out she was usually joined by her pals, Darky's wife and Stuffan's wife. Time flew by as the three of them chatted away and in the quiet summer air you heard the clicking of their knitting needles as they knitted socks – their hands were never idle. The ball of wool used to be tucked into a sash-like garment round their waist and packed up at the back to take the weight of the creel – it was called a

dronnag. The downside for me was that I had
to walk home – they never came home with an
empty creel!

Nowadays fewer people carry on cutting but more and more
are realising that there is much to be gained by burning
peat in our health-conscious, energy-hungry lives. The
compensation for all the honest toil is not just on the
financial and practical level, as Chrissie MacLean of
Stornoway relates: 'A day at the peats had its compensations.
The companionship, the cheerful banter, and the wonderful
taste of tea brewed in the fresh moorland air. It is easy to
forget the sore muscles, the cold, wet, days and the tortuous
midges.' Kristine Kennedy of Lochs agrees: 'There were
compensations though, forget Elizabeth Arden and Estée
Lauder, what hand cream can compare to a fresh peat?'
　　Peat cutting is a process that has not altered for centuries;
the development of the process has produced the most
efficient method for the Lewisman to obtain fuel. In 1920,
Marcel Hardy, the eminent botanist and geographer,
produced a survey entitled 'Prospects of Commercial
Agriculture in Lewis' for the new proprietor, Lord Leverhulme,
who had purchased the island from the Matheson family
the previous year. In the document, he includes a critical
analysis of the established methods employed for cutting
and drying peat with suggestions for improvements. It is a
passionate and informed document reflecting Hardy's
enthusiasm for peat. At one point he proclaims to the world:
'The day of the peat has come!'
　　However, his observations on Lewis led him to conclude
that: 'Lack of method in peat cutting is almost as objectionable as one could make it.' Hardy bemoans the 'anarchy'
of peat cutters who appear to cut peat when, where and
how they like. He was a keen promoter of the proper placing

of turf for the restoration of grazing, drainage and sustaining the land surface, even quoting Donald Munro's by-law that turf must be replaced. (The writer recalls being allocated a peat bank in the mid-1970s by the Stornoway Trust Factor, with the only advice given being: 'Make sure you replace the turf properly and look after the bank', said with an earnestness that suggested repercussions!) The consequences of the anarchic peat working were so serious that, according to one crofter Hardy spoke to, villages were abandoned. At Shader, between Barvas and Ness on the West side of Lewis, the access to a small hamlet towards the shore had become so dangerous as a result of the haphazard digging of the peat that the village had been quite recently abandoned and the inhabitants moved to the main road.

Hardy's answer to all this chaos was simple – co-operation. He proposed that families and whole villages should estimate how much peat would be needed and cut one big bank – each family cutting what they needed. The produce would be pooled, with each family taking equal amounts of good and poor quality peat. This would need a lot of organisation but Hardy had the answer:

> Indeed, a clever school master with the spirit of tradition and organisation might easily arrange the work so as to revise the old work-play, whereby the work was rhythmed by dance or song (as in the waulking of the Tweed) ensuring efficiency by suppressing irksomeness. Trenches must be planned and dug by the very process of peat cutting and a few acres reclaimed each year in view of croft extension. All this obviously requires a little thinking and organisation in every rural community. The school master is indicated

as the engineer as well as the only real moral authority in Lewis at the present day.

The teacher as the implementor of someone else's half-baked ideas was always the case. In conclusion, Hardy tempers his social engineering tendencies with sympathy for the crofters; their wisdom is the one that counts when it comes to change: 'They will only take to machine cut peats after they are quite convinced.'

His words were quite prophetic. Attempts were made to mechanise peat cutting in the 1980s with the introduction of 'sausage peats', cut using a device like a giant sausage machine pulled along a few feet under the ground behind a powerful tractor. This produced a continuous sausage of peat about six inches in diameter which broke up into short lengths on drying. Although this rapid technique dispensed with the cutting and throwing of the peat, it still required the peats to be lifted and gathered. The sausage shape proved awkward for building the peat stack so that it would readily stand up and shed water. Coming from near the surface, the peat often burned rapidly, and the process required extensive, well-drained flat land to begin with. It didn't catch on, although in certain areas of the island crofters persevere with the innovation as time becomes a precious commodity. Some resourceful crofters have used or adapted mechanical mini-diggers to extract peat but, for those with time to spare, the *tarasgair* remains the cutting edge of peat-cutting technology.

Although essential at one time, peat cutting rapidly declined with the coming of cheap, readily available heating oil and wood pellets, and the activity has become an alternative as life-style and expectations have changed. The 'Marmite' quality of people's love/hate relationship with peat cutting has probably helped the decline. In a world where complexity seems to be the rationale and personal isolation and social fragmentation appear close by, the simple task of cutting peat seems to be a just cause; a touchstone for man's dependence on himself, his neighbours and his surroundings. However, as Matthew MacIver of Portnaguran reflects, quoting the words of the Ardnamurchan crofter Alasdair MacLean, there is definitely a spirituality to peat cutting if you care to look for it: 'You leave home, maybe early on a spring morning, with the sun shining and a pleasant breeze blowing. You take a picnic lunch with you for you intend to stay all day and neither expect nor want to see anyone until you return at dusk. And you start to work at a job which has a direct and physical connection with who and what and why you are.'

On such a day, he argues, you would have to be a fool 'not to feel close to the beating heart of the world, not to feel accepted and nourished.'

When the peat began to be exploited for use by Matheson's Lewis Chemical Works in 1857, it wasn't the first time the Lewis moors had proved to be an industrial resource. In 1833 there was a steady trade between Stornoway and Leith, where peats were shipped to fire the malt kilns to improve the flavour of whisky. It was a valuable cargo fetching 13s 3d [67p] per ton at Leith. Matheson's venture however, would depend very much on developments happening in other parts of Britain in the 1840s; on the peat lands of Dartmoor and Devon in the south, and on the vast peat bogs of central Ireland in the west.

Chapter Two

The Peat of Dartmoor and the Bogs of Ireland

Dartmoor, topped by its windswept, granite tors, lies like a blister of wilderness erupting from the lush countryside and fertile valleys of South Devon. But, for all its bleakness, the moor was still a productive land in the 1840s, both on the barren land surface and in the depths below ground. Below the surface, the mines were a very important source of metals – tin, copper, silver and lead – while on the ground there were endless tracts of peat available for industrial and domestic fuel.

By the mid-1840s, Henry Caunter's interest in the natural world was becoming very influential in his life. He had become the manager of the West Beam and Silverbrook mines just a few miles from Ashburton while living in 'Linchover' – now called Ponsworthy House – in nearby Widecombe-in-the-Moor. There were many such mines in the region and the industry was thriving: it would be ten years or so before the import of cheap foreign metals was to signal the demise of the ancient industry.

The extraction of the metals from their ores was achieved with a piece of chemistry called smelting. The mineral ores – the rocks containing the metals – were simply heated with charcoal obtained from the peat. The charcoal, so obtained, was superior to the more commonly used coke, produced from coal, because it contained fewer impurities, notably sulphur.

Charcoal production, which had been taking place on Dartmoor since the thirteenth century, involved the process of burning peat in crude granite kilns called meilors with a limited supply of air in much the same way as charcoal is produced today from wood. After a few days of gentle smouldering, the fire in the mound was damped down and the kiln allowed to cool before opening to reveal the charcoal. The peat of Dartmoor was cut in a similar fashion and using similar tools to the way in which it is still cut in Lewis today.

In 1844, some sophistication and refinement was introduced into charcoal production by the British Patent Naphtha Company, started by Peter Adams and Jacob Hall-Drew with the backing of financial speculators in Plymouth. Besides charcoal, a whole range of other products were obtained from the peat, for which there was a developing market – illuminating oil (sold as Peatine), varnishes, paints, rubber solvent, moth-balls, candles and a gas for lighting. To obtain these products the peat was made to undergo the process of distillation. In the process of distillation, the peat was heated in the absence of air, or in a very limited supply of air, and the gases so produced were cooled and condensed to give tar which could be further treated to produce naphtha, the starting point for many of the products.

The works were set up in a former bakery near Princetown in the centre of Dartmoor. The peat came from the nearby

Greena Ball and Holming Beam areas of the moor, originally brought in by pack-horse, but subsequently on a horse-drawn tramway. By 1846, the works had moved to the vacant Dartmoor prison – built to house prisoners from the Napoleonic wars – and they were consuming thirty tons of peat per day. The venture provided work for many people, especially during the cutting season from April to September, but the company did not last the year. The British Patent Naphtha Company ceased after just a few years having burned a massive £29,000, a failure which has been attributed to poor management and extravagant expenditure on unsuitably engineered works. In the 1870s, when the prison was once again used for its intended purpose, convicts cut the peat and distillation started afresh, but this time the aim was to produce gas to light the prison, where the gas was noted for its good illuminating power.

In 1846, a second naphtha works opened at Redlake mire, just south of Ashburton, under the management of Messrs Davy and Wilkin of Totnes. They were involved at the time with the Ashburton Gas Works: since the production of town gas from coal is also carried out by the process of distillation, the two businesses may have been connected. Again the naphtha works didn't last long and the partnership was dissolved in 1850.

There can be no doubt that all this novel industry and technology was noted by the keen, inquisitive Henry Caunter who lived and worked alongside the developments. Perhaps this is when the seed of an idea was sown in his mind which would germinate the following decade into the Lewis Chemical Works. In September 1845, Caunter and Matheson sat down together to dine in Lewis, at which time the wise men of the Royal Society were considering Matheson's application for Fellowship with the citation: 'Attached to science and anxious to promote its progress.' The idea of possibly making money from his investment in Lewis would have appealed to the man. Within a few years peat distillation was being discussed on Lewis but with local opposition, so it would be a while before the first industrial peats were cut. The catalyst for this was events which were taking place in the extensive peat bogs of central Ireland.

The crofters of Lewis weren't the only people to be suffering from destitution in the 1840s. The peasantry of Ireland at that time was suffering terribly. The potato blight was rampant in that island and, as the potato was the currency of the day for the labourer, they were at the mercy of the disease. So dire was the situation that, by the early 1850s, the population of Ireland had fallen by about 20% as disease and starvation killed people in their hundreds of thousands and emigration carried many from their homeland to seek a better life.

Schemes were proposed to create income for the labouring classes – and wealth for the land owners – by developing the untapped, natural resources of Ireland. Fishing and the growing of flax were encouraged. In 1846, a plan was put forward by the Dublin engineer Jasper W Rogers to exploit the enormous, unproductive peat bogs of central Ireland. A few years earlier Rogers had taken out a patent for a process to produce charcoal from peat, cleverly using the waste heat from the furnace to dry the fresh-cut, wet peat such that it could be worked in a week. This reduced one of the major problems of using peat as a raw material: before it could be subjected to any process it had to be dried and traditional air drying methods could take many weeks and depend largely on the weather.

Peat charcoal was a commodity with great commercial potential. As the metal smelters of Dartmoor had known for years, its sulphur-free nature made it very attractive to the smelting industry. Its disinfecting and deodorising qualities made it very attractive for rendering human waste odourless and safer to handle and dispose of. At the time human waste – or night-soil as it was known – was collected in foul-smelling cesspits which had to be emptied when full, usually at night and often to be used as fertiliser. Rogers demonstrated that the night-soil could be made virtually odour-free and easy to handle. Compelling scientific investigations by Justus von Leibig showed that charcoal could help fertilisers to absorb substances for release to growing plants and this lead to farmers being encouraged to use the substance in powdered form on their fields.

In 1848, the Irish Amelioration Society was established by Royal Charter to 'give employment to the peasantry in the manufacture of peat charcoal', with Rogers as managing director and chief engineer. In September 1850 The Illustrated London News reporter and lithographer were on hand to record the scene when the first works (or station as it was called) went into production at Derrymullen, in Kildare, and between 300 and 800 people were variously reported to be employed in producing about 27,000 tons of charcoal an hour using Rogers' furnaces. The Charter required Rogers to build about 200 such stations which would have employed between 60,000 and 160,000 labourers; a vast number. At a time when destitution was rampant, such a tried and tested scheme to provide employment could not be ignored.

Rogers had done his market research and estimated that London alone required 200,000 tons of charcoal to treat its cesspits and that: 'The constructing parties were ready to receive the article as soon as it was ready for exportation – the sooner, they said, the better.' So reported the Edinburgh Advertiser in 1850.

Rogers' ambitious schemes had a bonus: the land, once cleared of peat, would be drained and could be put to productive, agricultural use. If ever Matheson needed ideas for dealing with the problems of Lewis, he didn't have to look far for inspiration. Rogers opened up offices in London,

Dublin and Bristol with a view to cleaning up the nation with his charcoal and proceeded to give public demonstrations of its efficiency in dealing with human waste. Samples of the charcoal even made it as far as Inverness where a public demonstration was arranged by Mr Kennedy McNab in October 1850. McNab was in the process of trying to establish a peat charcoal manufactory at Ferrintosh, near Inverness, to produce pulverised peat charcoal for agricultural use. Rogers even made it to the exposé of all that was wonderful about 1851 Britain – the Great Exhibition. 'The day of the peat' was surely about to dawn.

Unfortunately, the night-soil was about to hit the fan. Rogers had reckoned without that influential body of jobsworths, The Metropolitan Commission for Sewers, who decreed that London's 200,000 smelly cesspits should be closed; the very cesspits which were to have received Rogers' charcoal. Instead, drains were to be connected to open sewers feeding into the Thames where the annoying night-soil would simply float away. In trying to solve the problem of smell, the Commission had exacerbated a bigger and more dangerous issue and terrible cholera epidemics hit the town, carrying away many Londoners to their deaths. It would be a while before Joseph Bazelgette and his scheme of underground sewers resolved the problem.

By 1852 the Irish Amelioration Society had ceased and in 1853, Rogers was in the debtor's court with all his assets frozen. Using the new science Rogers had tried to champion the cause of the Irish peasantry – he wrote pamphlets on the subject – and at the same time to make money for his backers while solving the hygiene problems of the large cities. It had been shown on Dartmoor that peat is a difficult resource to exploit on an industrial scale but all these failures did not deter others, including James Matheson, from taking up the challenge.

Chapter Three

Success in Ireland

'The Irish bogs would be more valuable than all the
gold regions of California'
– Lord Ashley

While Rogers was trying to raise interest in his schemes,
the exploitation of Irish peat made a far more alluring call
on the speculators, and that call went out from a place
which would certainly cause people to take notice. On July
27th 1849, James Patrick Mahon – or The O'Gorman Mahon
as he called himself – the MP for Ennis (and later a soldier
of fortune) spoke in the House of Commons, at the end of
a debate on the Irish Poor Law, to read out a letter he had
received from a London chemist, Dr John Waters:

> I beg to acquaint you that a discovery has been
> made in Ireland and which will materially
> enhance the value of landed property in that
> country. It consists in the aptitude of its millions
> of peat acres to produce at trifling expense – little
> more than that of manual labour – oil, naphtha,

candles, tar, etc by a new process of distillation …
I have no hesitation in pronouncing it as one of
the greatest discoveries of the age and one which
will become a source of unbounded wealth.

Mahon spoke further, listing testimonies for his assertions from such luminaries as Professor Justus von Liebig of Giessen University and Dr Hodges, Chemistry professor at Belfast University. Mahon then produced a small candle made of peat wax which brought light to his words by burning with a steady, brilliant flame, lighting up the House of Commons.

Mahon was supported in his revelations by Lord Ashley, who proceeded to give a character reference for Mr Owen who had carried out the investigation to produce the peat products. Lord Ashley knew Owen as a personal acquaintance and described him as 'a discrete, sober, generous, high-minded, religious man … a person incapable of making an exaggerated statement.'

Ashley went on to reveal that the distillation process, by which the peat was converted into very saleable products, could show a considerable profit. For the cost of £16 for labour and processing, a return of £92 could be expected on sales, and in addition the land would be transformed into a condition which would support agriculture. Lord Ashley described how Owen had arrived at these figures by experimenting on thousands of tons of peat for over 12 months and that he was a man who wished for 'no recompense or reward from the country. His object was to confer benefit on Ireland and to show that there existed in that country a profitable investment for money which had never hitherto been dreamed of.'

Finally, although Lord Ashley recommended that a degree of caution be taken concerning what he had just said, he ended his statement to the House with a flourish, sending the Members off at a late hour – the sitting adjourned at 11 pm – to enjoy the weekend by contemplating fortunes to be made: 'if only one half of the results which he had indicated were to be realised, the effect would be most extraordinary and beneficial; indeed, in such the case, 100,000 acres of Irish bog would be more valuable than all the gold regions of California.'

It is not known if James Matheson was in the House of Commons to hear the O'Gorman Mahon and Lord Ashley announce their discovery and witness the burning peat candle. His brother, Col. Thomas Matheson – now the MP for Ashburton – definitely was present and would have seen first-hand the possibilities of the night's revelations. There is no doubting that James would have been intrigued to discover that his investment in Lewis might turn out to be the best financial stake he had ever made.

The following day, the London newspapers were full of the story. The Standard thought it to be 'of the greatest importance as a physical discovery and an inexhaustible resource of material nature,' ranking peat distillation alongside steam navigation, railroads and agricultural chemistry as achievements of the age. By Monday morning – the announcement had been made late on Friday night – the news of the possibility of a good investment had, according to the Times, 'attracted considerable attention in the city and excited strong hopes of extensive results.' Things were looking rosy again; the day of the peat was not yet over.

Over the next few days, correspondence in the Times indicated that the situation seemed too good to be true. Henry Seaman, one of the investors in the British Patent Naphtha Company, was quick to warn would-be speculators that £29,000 had been spent and lost on an identical adventure just three years previously, in the peat bogs of Dartmoor. Despite having an able chemist as manager and six able directors who were merchants and tradesmen, 'somehow or other it was a failure.'

A couple of days later, letters from both Lord Ashley and Mr Owen appeared in the Times, which must have depressed any excitement the city was feeling. Lord Ashley wished to clarify his position; rather than expressing knowledge of peat distillation he was merely providing a character reference for Mr Owen who had provided him with the 'facts'. Owen's letter painted a somewhat different picture of the 'facts'. He wished to point out that, rather than spending a vast fortune experimenting on a thousand tons of peat and making a good return – as Lord Ashley had indicated, having allegedly been informed by Owen – he had actually experimented on just twenty tons of peat, spent £1,000 and made no profitable return.

The press was quick to sense an over-egging of the pudding. The leader of the Morning Chronicle of 6th August cautioned would-be investors that the process of peat distillation, described as new, was well known; that all the products of peat distillation were readily available and produced on an enormous scale from coal, shale and wood; that the practicalities and costs involved in working peat and purifying the products were unknown. They concluded with a probable reference to Rogers' endeavours: 'Exaggerations of this kind do serious mischief. The comparative failure of each over-rated scheme tends to throw discredit on more sober undertakings and prevent steady investment into Irish improvements.' They then signed off:

"Tis a pity when sanguine statesmen
Speak on subjects they don't understand.'

82

Correspondence rumbled on with veiled support for the scheme from Robert Oxland, another of the Plymouth venturers, whilst those with a competing commercial interest heaped scorn and scepticism on the matter.

This interest and speculation as to the worth of the distillation of Irish peat was not solely a matter for the London press. On 10th August, the London correspondent of the Inverness Courier lampooned that night of the peat wax candle in the House of Commons with a vision for the future and of the rôle the Hebrides would play;

> Lord Ashley – a discrete, pains-taking, matter-of-fact man – was tempted to declare this to be the greatest discovery of the age and that 100,000 acres of Irish peat moss are worth more than all the gold-digging of California. Why, then, the Isle of Lewis will be found more valuable than the [diamond] mines of Golconda or the Sycee silver mines of China or the cinnamon groves or coffee fields of Ceylon or the spicy productions of the Philippine Isles and Araby the Blest ... The Lothians and the fertile plains of Essex will be demanding protection against the overflowing productiveness of Uist and the emigration to Australia will be diverted to the Hebrides.

Henry Caunter and James Matheson would have been smiling if they read the jest but it would have set them thinking again. The possibilities of developing the peat bogs of Lewis would definitely have appealed to Matheson; he too was faced with a tenantry suffering from hardship and little work, and he was the owner of a large tract of unproductive peat bog. His hopes and sensibilities of the rôle he wanted science to play in the development of Lewis would be fulfilled. One can hear the conversations between Henry Caunter and James Matheson, both face-to-face and by letter. The gifted, passionate and convincing Henry, who had first come to Lewis in 1845 so that, in the words of Roderick Morrison, 'in the course of his scientific researches, [the island's] hidden treasures may come to light,' and Matheson, the ruthless, enthusiastic merchant who listened, read and thought.

Between 1849 and 1853, the distillation of local peat was discussed on Lewis but any plans or ideas that Matheson may have had were put on hold on the advice of his factor, John Munro MacKenzie. In a letter to Hugh Matheson, commissioner for Sir James Matheson, written in 1878 and published under the title 'Island of Lews and its Fishermen Crofters', Donald MacKinlay, a native of Stornoway, clearly states the position, referring to the discontinuation of Matheson's improvements: 'One of the works – the 'Chemical Works' – costing £33,000 was executed contrary to the advice of Mr Munro MacKenzie.'

Munro Mackenzie knew what he was talking about. As an engineer and business manager, a man who knew the land and who knew the people of Lewis, he had the wherewithal to form an honest, informed and objective view of the possibilities for peat distillation on Lewis. Matheson must have valued Munro MacKenzie's wise counsel; he had the good sense to wait until Munro MacKenzie departed in 1853 before he proceeded with his scheme for the Lewis Chemical Works.

What was behind these tales and promises – of wealth for landlords and freedom from poverty and grind for those living on the moors of Ireland and Scotland? And how did peat distillation become a subject for the floor of the House of Commons?

The process of distillation has always been an important part of man's investigation of the substances around him.

The ancient alchemists used distillation in their search for the Philosopher's Stone; that mystical substance which, it was thought, would convert metals like tin, lead and copper into gold and so secure a quick fortune. They also sought the Elixir of Life which they thought would confer eternal youth, using strange pieces of apparatus – alembics, pellicons and retorts – to distil, for example, eggs, which they believed contained the 'breath of life'. By the beginning of the sixteenth century Friar Cor was a pioneer of Scottish distilling, making aqua vitae, or whisky, by distilling wine, in a well-established industry. By the seventeenth century, the process of distillation was being put to a more practical use. Nicolas le Fevre, one of the original Fellows of the Royal Society, and who was Apothecary Royal to Charles the second, records in 1668, in his *Compleat Body of Chemistry*, the distillation of urine to produce 'Igneous Spirit of Urine' which was the universal medicine 'of a sovereign efficacy in allaying the pain of all parts of the body and is a very excellent remedy against Epileptical, Apoplectical and Maniacal Diseases and all other of the like nature.'

About the same time Johan Glauber noted that, on distilling wood in a brick oven, he collected 'a sharp hot Oyl of a dark reddish colour', which was useful for preserving wood and protecting fruit trees from insect attack. Today, it is called creosote. He also distilled coal but did not record the production of any inflammable gas which was first discovered by Rev John Clayton in 1680, although his work was not published until 1740.

By 1800, chemistry was being applied to the developing Industrial Revolution. The Scottish inventor and engineer, William Murdoch, produced a successful gas light while investigating coal gas, obtained from the distillation of coal. In 1807, the Lyceum Theatre and Pall Mall, in London, were being lit by his new gas. It was the way forward. Gas was convenient; it could be piped to where it was to be burned and it was easy to control. However there would be no instant switch from tallow candles and oil lamps to gas lighting. Opposition from those with vested interests in oil and tallow, the approaching near extinction of whales – the blubber of which was the source of much illuminating oil – and the suspected dangers of coal gas ensured a gradual change. As gas works developed, the other products of coal distillation – tar, ammonia liquor and coke – were investigated, as were the similar substances obtained from wood and peat.

In 1833, the German chemist, Carl Reichenbach had managed to obtain a new solid wax from beech tar while investigating the distillation of beech wood. He called the new wax paraffin, literally meaning 'little affinity' as it did not seem to react with anything. It was soon found to be an excellent wax for making candles as it burned with a bright flame, but its drawback was the expense in purifying the crude wax. Confusingly, the word paraffin was also used to describe the combustible oil that could be obtained from distilling coal or wood.

In 1847, the scientist Lyon Playfair, who was later to take an interest in the Lewis Chemical Works, noticed oil seeping from a coal seam in a Derbyshire mine. He brought this to the attention of the Scottish chemist, James Young, who managed to produce paraffin oil, which he marketed as an alternative oil for lighting to replace the declining stocks of whale oil. This source in the coal mine unexpectedly ran out but, in 1850, he patented a method for distilling shale – a mineral commonly found across central Scotland and occurring nearer to the surface than coal – to produce paraffin oil suitable for lighting. By 1851, he had set up the world's first commercial oil works at Bathgate in West Lothian to extract, initially, naphtha and lubricating oils and, by 1856, paraffin oil for lamps which soon became available nationally. Gas, paraffin oil and paraffin wax (candles) all lit up the 1840s and 1850s as the smelly tallow candles and whale oil lamps gave way to progress. Any resource that could produce these chemicals was worth investigating. The commercial climate of the time was one of opportunity, optimism and hope; if one man should fail then the next must surely succeed.

It was in this climate of searching for new energy sources that Rees Reece, a Welsh chemist, was working in Paris, in the laboratory of M. Pellouse, where in the mid-1840s he developed a simple modification to the process of peat distillation. Previously distillation was carried out by two distinct methods; closed and open. In the closed method, the peat was heated in a closed container called a retort and heated from outside using coal, wood or peat (as in Rogers' process). When the peat had been distilled, the process had to be stopped so that the retort could be emptied of peat charcoal and replaced with a fresh batch of peat. In the open process the peat was placed in a container with an open base and hearth called a kiln and set on fire at the base. The heat produced from the burning peat caused the peat above in the kiln to distil. As the burning peat at the base turned to ash, charcoal produced from the distilled peat fell into the hearth and became the fuel which burned to keep the process going as fresh peat was continually added at the top of the kiln. In both processes the gas and the vapours of tar and watery liquid (liquor) were drawn off from the top of the retort or kiln and led to a condenser where the tar and the liquor vapours were cooled and turned into a liquid. This made the open process one which could be kept going continuously, twenty-four hours a day.

Reece's modification of the open furnace process was simple; he sent a blast of air up through the kiln, which gave two major advantages. Firstly, the peat at the base of the kiln burned better and secondly, the products of distillation were rapidly driven from the kiln which avoided their decomposing in the heat. On January 29th 1849 Reece was granted a patent (No. 12436) for 'Treating Peat and obtaining Products there- from'. One of the clauses in the patent was significant: 'of obtaining products from peat which I call paraffine and liquid paraffin.' Reece was producing wax and paraffin which could rival Young.

The treatment of the tar to produce paraffin involved a simple, cheap piece of chemistry which would replace the more expensive methods then in use. The patent certainly had commercial possibilities – untapped raw materials (peat) and a new superior product (paraffin). The subsequent development of the patent specifications were to have a considerable bearing on the course of the Lewis Chemical Works, forming the basis of its working principle.

In order to develop his discoveries, Reece needed a backer and found one in Mr Owen, a wealthy London linen draper of Great Coram Street. The Government also showed an interest in these developments in the world of peat distillation – political, scientific and technological – and asked Sir Robert Kane, Director of the Museum of Irish Industry, to investigate the matter as to its commercial viability and report back.

In the meantime Reece and Owen pressed on with their venture at Newtown Crommelin, west of Belfast in the north of Ireland, with what would nowadays be called a pilot plant to investigate the feasibility of a large commercial works. To raise more capital, Reece produced a prospectus for the 'British and Irish Peat Company' quoting his assessment of annual expenditure and income based on the results of experiments from the pilot plant which had been carried out under the supervision of Dr Hodges, Professor of Agriculture and Chemistry at Queens College, Belfast. Reece had also managed to secure various other patents and a Royal Charter of Incorporation was obtained to enable operations to start on a full scale.

In September 1849, the appointment of Sir Robert Kane to report on peat distillation prompted the editor of the Pharmaceutical Journal to include an article entitled 'California in Ireland', in which Reece's progress was reviewed; the men of science were getting excited. (Twenty years later, the editor of that same journal was Dr Benjamin Paul who was to develop the Lewis Chemical Works a decade after Reece's work in Ireland). In early January 1851 Charles Dickens published an article similarly titled 'The Irish California' in his weekly magazine, 'Household Words', bringing Reece's venture to the wider public. It is written in a clear, informative, easy style which Reece himself referred to as 'authoritative'. The author manages to make the technology and chemistry quite accessible but was not, unfortunately, credited. He ends the piece full of hope, comparing the venture to the deeds of St Patrick: 'They [the Irish] will probably have much more reason to thank Mr Rees Reece and Mr Owen for the opulence which these gentlemen will have conjured out of the bogs by the beautiful magic of chemistry aided by capital.'

Then, on 8th April 1851, Kane's report, 'The Nature and Products of the Destructive Distillation of Peat', was handed to Lord Seymour to be presented to both Houses of Parliament. On 30th June 1851 it was laid on the table of the House of Commons and the following day was presented in the House of Lords.

The report had two aims; a scientific examination of the results of the distillation of peat and a practical considera-tion of the economy of the process on an industrial scale. The report was thorough and, such was the meticulous nature and clarity of the study, it was still being referred to fifty years later in scientific works on the subject. The conclusions did not just apply to Irish peat but could be applied to the working of peat in any location, including the Isle of Lewis.

Kane concluded that Reece's results were not exaggerated, but that the products obtained from peat could be obtained more economically from coal. Any peat manufactory would need to be run on the most economical of lines to make it competitive and because of the remote location of peat deposits, would necessarily require new and complex processes to be carried out at one site rather than with specialist contractors. This gloomy outlook was balanced by one very positive conclusion: 'Paraffin may be an exception. It is a material new to commerce on a large scale and its value is not determined by comparative economy.' Kane's final conclusion was full of hope for the development of peat distillation; that the expected overcoming of difficulties should be regarded as of 'very great interest and public utility' and that manufactories should be established, especially in Ireland. Preparing the report must have impressed Kane as to the potential of peat, pointing out that 'whereas Englishmen could boast of a wealth of fuel underground [coal], Ireland has a similar wealth on the surface.'

This was music to the ears of Reece, Owen and their backers: positive confirmation of their work tempered with encouragement and caution; laying an emphasis on working margins; and having a product with an edge in paraffin. The conclusions were well-reported in the press, no doubt fuelling any discussions on the subject between James Matheson and John Munro MacKenzie and giving Henry Caunter cause for excitement.

Meanwhile, Rees Reece proceeded to erect a factory at Athy on the Bog of Allen, south-west of Dublin, of a much larger and more efficient design than his starter plant. The two kilns and single condenser of the pilot plant were replaced with four large kilns and a double row of eight condensers backed up with 'scrubber towers' to condense all the tar. The design plan bears an amazing similarity to the works which were to be erected in the Isle of Lewis just a few years later, despite being protected by patents. Progress seems to have been good and Reece continued to develop his design; in 1854, he was granted a patent which allowed him to use the kiln to smelt iron ore at the same time as he was distilling peat.

He also appears to have heeded Kane's advice and concentrated on paraffin as the major product from which he produced candles 'of the most exquisite transparency, rivalling the best wax lights in brilliancy and combustion.' So wrote Charles Weld during his visit to Ireland in the mid-1850s, when he was given a conducted tour of the factory by the manager, Reece himself. Weld was impressed, commenting on the recycling of the gas, which was produced in the distillation, as a fuel, and of the possibility of using any charcoal produced as a disinfectant. He recorded that the production, or refining, of the paraffin was sub-contracted but, such was the economy of the production of the crude paraffin, it was selling at the prospectus-projected price of the refined wax. Weld reported that the annual shareholders meeting had been given a favourable report on progress; improvements had been made to the supply of peat and to the production of the paraffin. The profit after all expenditure was put at £75 a week, enough for the repayment of interest, loans and advances.

Weld was probably known to James Matheson; from 1845 to 1860 he was librarian and historian at the Royal Society in whose Burlington House premises he lived. He also wrote a number of travel and science books; *Vacations in Ireland* was published in 1857 and was reviewed in the Spectator magazine, which included an extensive quote from the chapter on the Irish Peat Company.

By the time the Spectator article appeared in 1857, peat distillation was a more solid bet for the investor. It had been given the seal of approval, both as a subject for study by the men of science in what would nowadays be called a peer-review, and as a process for commercial pursuit by the men of power in the form of a Government report. In Ireland Reece had shown that, with careful planning and listening to wise heads, a profit could be turned from peat distillation.

Sometime between 1853 and 1856, Henry Caunter left Devon and came to stay as Matheson's man-of-science in Lews Castle, where he made a start on his own grand work of peat distillation – the Lewis Chemical Works. The day of the peat had come!

PART THREE

The Lewis Chemical Works

Chapter One

The Candle Works

'... the gentleman at the Castle (Mr Caunter) was
to make Candles out of peat.'
– Donald Morison

In mid-September 1857, the Inverness Advertiser correspondent filed a report after a trip to Lewis: 'The crops here
are remarkably good, justifying the expenditure which has
been so liberally applied. The improvements are being still
vigorously proceeded with, so much so, indeed that
throughout the island no one willing to work remains
unemployed.'

Things appeared to be looking good for the people of
Lewis. Earlier in the year, in April 1857, James Matheson
had been re-elected, unopposed, as MP for Ross and
Cromarty, a seat he had held since 1847. In Stornoway there
were triumphal celebrations on his return to power; the
hoisting of flags, the booming of guns and much feasting
for the estate workers, culminated in them parading three
times around Lews Castle behind Sir James' pibroch-playing
piper, cheering loudly.

In May of that year, the Stornoway ship yard of Mr Cook was busy and the 150 ton schooner *Lady Matheson* was launched by Captain Donald MacKenzie. The fishing was looking hopeful with a large fleet of 400 fishing boats in the harbour and, with upwards of 3,000 'hardy sons of Neptune', the town would have been buzzing. Matheson probably felt a sense of achievement that things were going right. He was now free from the constraining wisdom of John Munro MacKenzie and free to explore his scientific and commercial interests in further developing Lewis. It was time for some indulgence on a grand scale.

Sometime in the mid-1850s, Henry Caunter had moved to Stornoway from Ashburton, staying initially at the Castle as a guest of Matheson before moving to Glen House. He was to remain in Lewis for the rest of his life, most of which would be spent chasing his dreams of scientific discovery. On 10th September 1857, the Inverness Courier gave a detailed report of the Lewis Farming Society's annual exhibition. After dinner in the Lews Hotel, chaired by James Matheson, there was much talk and relaxation:

> Amongst other discussions, the party were entertained with a lucid description, on the part of Mr Caunter, late of Ashburton, of the process of distilling oil from peats and the various purposes to which it can be applied, as now conducted by him on the island. His scientific acquirements, we trust, will turn the large masses of peat in the Lews to beneficial uses for the behoof of the worthy proprietor.

A few days later the Inverness Advertiser's correspondent, waxed lyrical about his recent visit to Lewis: 'I was shown a specimen of a candle made from peat and was informed that some experiments are going on as to rendering available for this and other purposes the peat extracts.' The repercussions of that other peat wax candle, lit eight years earlier in the House of Commons by the O'Gorman Mahon, were finally being seen in Stornoway.

Although Henry Caunter was a wealthy man in his own right, he was quite happy to pass on the financial burden in order to start his investigations. Matheson had confidence in Caunter to develop Lewis peat bogs on a scientific basis, despite the failure of other projects, and was quite willing to underwrite the venture, as Donald Morison relates;

> Having great influence with Sir James and Lady Matheson whose well Known Generosity and unsparing hand, spent large sums of Money on Works with the aim of benefiting and improving the condition of the overplus, unskilled Labour on the Lewis Estate, which in many cases proved discouraging for further outlay. Nevertheless, Sir James did not hesitate in allowing Mr Caunter to proceed with experiments with the hope of Utilising the unproductive Peat Bogs of the Estate.

Henry started by experimenting at the edge of a fish pond close to the Castle but this did not last very long and the fish soon died as a result of pollution. Instead, an experimental works was built on moorland about 200 metres west of the Lochs road, south of Stornoway, just opposite the Creed Lodge entrance to the Castle grounds. This works was sited near to a burn leading to the river Creed, prized for its salmon fishing (the burn is known to this day, locally, as the Paraffin Burn). Again fish died – Henry was having a bad start. The foundations of the stone-built works can still be seen today at the end of a track leading from the main road. Through 1857, Henry slowly laboured away with his kiln and condenser and by the end of the year had managed to produce about half a ton of crude peat tar.

Caunter was assisted in his work by Robert Wilson, a native of Auchtermuchty in Fife, who, at various times had been manager of Matheson's Gas and Water works in Stornoway. Wilson was an ideal assistant for Caunter; his experience of making gas and coke from coal by the established process of distillation would have been useful in designing the kiln and condenser for Caunter's chemical works. Wilson was an able and intelligent man of many talents – a plumber, fishing net barker, tinsmith and clock-repairer – as Morison describes him with his eye for detail:

> Wilson was considered in Stornoway and all over the island the authority of any job requiring ingenuity, would take in hand to improve the compleatest steam or other engine ever invented, a first Class Judge of a Dram whether foreign or home Manufacture. Overall an agreeable little man 8½ stone weight 5' 6" high.

John Munro MacKenzie refers to Wilson in his diary of 1851, in which he confides that he did not think Wilson was up to the job of Gas works manager: 'the [gas] works seem to do little more than pay expenses – I fear they will never do well under the present management.'

That was on February 25th and six months later, on August 13th, Wilson was discharged from his duties, examination of the books showing that the accounts had been 'short of about £16'. By 1861, he was back as manager, living with his wife Barbara and eight children at the Gas works, a position he occupied into the 1870s.

Gas works were important in Stornoway, providing gas and coke to light and heat the Castle and for lighting the streets of Stornoway. Lews Castle was lit with coal gas rather than gas produced from peat, probably due to the cost of supplying the peat. Coal was cheaper to use as the brickworks had shown, despite the abundance of local peat.

The production of gas from peat was well-known at this time. In the early spring of 1856 a lecture had been given to the Dublin Chemical Society on the benefits of using peat rather than coal for lighting. This was reported in the John O'Groat Journal, the column ending with the rejoinder: 'We hope to hear of some experiments in the far north [Lerwick], which may result in what is considered here a good gas at a cheap rate.'

At the 1857 meeting of the British Association for the Advancement of Science held in Dublin, R.L Johnson, in his closing remarks on a paper comparing the use of peat gas to coal gas, commented: 'Bogs may become under the influence of an enlightened energy, sources of wealth and industry, eminently productive.'

There would have been much labour involved in Caunter's schemes; from construction of the building for the works and the approach track from the main road, to cutting and gathering the peat and transporting it from the moor. The labourers were probably bemused at being paid for cutting peat, a job usually associated with unremitting toil, but they would have been happy to take the pennies. The peat was cut on the moorland stretching west of Henry's works and was transported into the works on a novel piece of engineering; a canal about a kilometre long and four metres wide.

The canal, which would have required much labour to build, ran across a gently sloping tract of moorland to the west of the works. The route of the canal was east-west and the peats were cut from the ground on its southern bank where the peat lay about two metres deep. To the north of the canal, the moor sloped gently down to the Paraffin Burn, which ran on a parallel course to the canal.

Long stretches of this canal still exist and hold water, a testament to its designers and builders. In May 1963, the Ordnance Survey were again mapping the island but this time from the air. The 1:7,500 scale aerial photograph of the area clearly shows the line of the canal, the peat banks, the Paraffin Burn and the site of the chemical works. This part of the moor has recently (2012) been disturbed by the laying of an underground electricity cable to connect the newly erected wind turbines on nearby Ben Hulabie to the electricity sub-station by the River Creed on the Lochs Road, a short distance from the site of Caunter's works. The moorland site through which the canal runs now has archae-ological and historical sensitivities and so, prior to the laying of the cable, a survey (an archaeological watching brief) was undertaken by local archaeologist Carol Knott. This allowed a close examination of the methods of construction and the materials used by Caunter and Wilson to construct the canal.

Since the canal was built across gently sloping ground, the down-slope bank required to be solid and firm to maintain the integrity of the structure and to keep the water in. Caunter and Wilson were up to the challenge. The Victorian attitude to engineering was one of creating permanent structures and the canal was no exception. There was no clay, rock, or timber to hand in the middle of the moor – the usual basic canal building materials – and so they used what was available – peat. The banks of the canal were built from the up-cast material from the digging of the canal, along with dried peats laid down to create a stable structure at the edge of the bank. Perhaps the inspiration came from the building of a peat stack; in any case it worked well.

Although a canal generally runs through varying topography, a constant water level is usually maintained by building cuttings and viaducts and using locks to control the water. On Caunter's canal this would have meant digging a cutting at the western end which would have made the loading of boats very difficult. They solved this problem by building essentially two canals, end-on to each other, following the same line and separated by about six metres of solid ground. This would have required peat to be transferred from one boat to another at a lower level, a drop of less than a metre. The higher (western end) canal also had an overflow ditch down to the Paraffin Burn, which was the source of the canal water at the western end of the canal. The peat cut to the south of the canal was dried and gathered at the edge of the canal for loading onto boats. To make the loading simple at water level, the southern bank was built away from the edge of the canal to create a semi-circular wharf stretching about six metres from the canal, where the peat could be gathered and stacked until required. The boats were probably dragged by manpower or ponies or were poled along, although sail could have been used if the wind was kind.

This system allowed Caunter and Wilson, with patience and slow modification of their apparatus, to produce about half a ton of crude peat tar of a sort throughout 1857. At this stage, the works were known as the Candle Works, as Donald Morison explained: 'It being reported and generally believed through the island that the Gentleman at the Castle (Mr Caunter) was to make Candles out of peat. Which gave the works the Name of Candle Works during its existence.'

The word 'distillation', prior to Henry Caunter's presence, had only one connotation in nineteenth-century Lewis – that of whisky production. So the excise men were soon sniffing around the Candle Works. Donald Morison wrote: 'It was rumoured that the excise men had discovered something else than peat was being distilled. But on examination it was proved that it was only a few Bottles of Glenlevet, which Wilson had hide about for his own requirements when fitting up the apparatus.'

After a month of experimenting Henry discovered a problem. Rees Reece had demonstrated that subtle but simple chemistry was needed to convert the crude peat tar into paraffin for producing candles and paraffin oil. Henry knew his limits as a chemist and could produce no candles. A keener chemical knowledge was needed.

During the summer and autumn of 1858 Matheson was in poor health, which led him to absent himself from the House of Commons. In doing so he invited the ire of the merchants of Inverness who felt aggrieved at his lack of interest and concern in representing them. Matheson claimed to have been advised to 'avoid any unusual exertion either of body or mind.' However, as the merchants pointed out, this had not stopped him from attending and influencing Railway Board meetings where he was a Director, or pursuing a chemist to advance Caunter's works.

In order to attract an enquiring mind and to enable a proper study of peat distillation and its exploitation, a laboratory was added to Glen House where Caunter lived, the building of which was contracted to one Donald Morison, stone-mason and native of Stornoway. Not only did Morison build the laboratory, but he went on to become a pivotal presence in the building, operation and preservation of the history of Lewis Chemical Works.

Chapter Two

Donald Morison, Stone Mason

'The truth is, of course, that there is no pure truth;
only the moody accounts of witnesses.'
Laurie Lee (I Can't Stay Long)

Donald Morison was to play a central role in the life of
the Lewis Chemical Works. He was the man who built the
works, according to the plans of Dr BH Paul, and the man
who learned to successfully operate the process of peat
distillation. He acted as foreman for the works for a number
of years after Paul left Lewis in 1862. He is also responsible
for writing, in 1895, an intimate history of the Lewis
Chemical Works, quirkily entitled 'The Beginning and the
End of the Lewis Chemical Works, 1857-1874', one of the
few documents of the time still available concerning
Matheson's ownership of the Isle of Lewis. A disastrous
Town Hall fire in Stornoway in 1918 destroyed all the
surviving estate papers of Matheson's tenure of the island.
Without this manuscript, the only other contemporary
written account – a scientific paper read by Dr Paul in
1862 describing his development of the works – would

probably have lain undiscovered in the annals of the Society of Arts.

Donald Morison was born in Stornoway on November 18th 1829, at 57 Bayhead Street, to Angus Morrison, a stone-mason, and Barbara Morison (unrelated). As he grew up, Donald – the eldest sibling, along with sister Kate (b.1834) and brother John (b.1844) – naturally turned to his father's trade of stone-mason. His father worked his trade on the gargoyles and staircase balustrade of the new Lews Castle which was being constructed in the late 1840s. It was at that time that Donald left Stornoway with little formal education to pursue his trade as a journeyman stone-mason in Glasgow, staying in lodgings in Paisley. He worked at one time on the pulpit of Glasgow Cathedral with his future father-in-law, James Nisbet. In the mid-1850s he married Elizabeth Nisbet, a native of Glasgow who was descended from John Nisbet, the seventeenth-century Covenanter. Donald was a talented man with an eye for business and his wife an able woman who had attended Glasgow High School. The couple thrived on life in Glasgow and trade flourished, as the Highland News reported: 'By dint of observation and industry combined with an ability and intelligence rarely found in one with so few educational advantages, he soon outstripped his fellow workmen and became an enterprising and successful business contractor.'

Donald and his wife moved into 213 Stirling Street and a family followed; Angus was born in 1854 and James in 1856, after the family had settled into apartments in Cowcaddens Street. The couple's successful life was soon to suffer tragic misfortune as, first, James died in infancy and then Donald suffered a bad accident whilst overseeing the erection of some extensive works in the city. This brought about a decision to move back to the Isle of Lewis, where the couple were to raise a family of seven boys and a girl:

Angus (b.1854), James (b.1860), Donald (b.1861), Mary-Jane (b.1865), Henry (b.1867), John (b.1869), George (b.1873) and Walter (b.1876). According to her birth certificate, Mary-Jane – who was named after James Matheson's wife – was recorded as having been born at 'the Lewis Chemical Works' where the family lived in a workman's cottage known as the Paraffin Works Cottage number 2.

The Chemical Works and the Garrabost Brick Works where the young Morisons spent their childhood, must have provided the ultimate children's playground. Bill Scott of St Andrews recalls his mother's tales of his grandmother, Mary-Jane Morison, who, with her brothers, would ride on peat hutches – trucks – on the tramway lines which had been laid throughout the peat banks to transport the peat. They used to raise a mast, hoist a sail, and bowl along! Whether this was a works practice or schoolboy ingenuity, Bill is unsure, but it sounds fun.

Donald Morison was first employed by Sir James Matheson in late 1858 or early 1859 when he was contracted to build an extension to Glen House (where Henry Caunter was then living) to house a laboratory for Dr Benjamin Paul who was appointed by Matheson in early 1858 to develop the Chemical Works from Caunter's initial scheme. The laboratory can still be seen as a single-storey extension at the eastern end of Glen House, which stands on the corner of Willowglen Road, opposite the Caberfeidh Hotel in Stornoway.

Donald's photographic portrait shows a man of thoughtful confidence, relaxed, gentle bearing and with an enquiring eye. The family was strict in the religious sense; Bill Scott describes how they drew the blinds to prevent being seen when polishing boots before going to church. Donald was not insensitive to life's simple pleasures; he was a reader and had read some Thomas Carlisle. From his comments about Wilson the Gas Works manager, Donald was not averse to enjoying a dram, although his son John was later to become a Rechabite and eschew the drink.

Donald had a strong regard for his fellow man and a sense of civic duty and involvement. Whilst living in Glasgow he was an active member of the Watch Committee, helping to preserve the peace in times of unrest before a regular police force was established. At the other end of the spectrum, a family tale tells of how he helped a young couple to elope whilst staying in Ireland on estate business. His sympathies were aroused by the plight of his own grandparents who had eloped from Glasgow to Oban where Donald's father was born. On a personal level, when Henry Caunter found himself in a difficult situation as manager of the Lewis Chemical Works, Donald was a loyal friend. In Henry's hour of need, Donald, although innocent, aligned himself with the scandalous position Henry had got himself into in order to 'mitigate his mind.'

His writings portray him as an industrious, enterprising and loyal diplomat with ability and intelligence. He was of the first generation of his family who could write; his father signed his name with an X. He was not afraid to speak his mind if he could not understand something or if he could see a problem, qualities which would undoubtedly attract him to James Matheson as a safe pair of hands. On one occasion, when Donald threatened to resign and return to good trade opportunities opening up in Glasgow, only the intervention of the proprietor himself could persuade Morison to stay at the Lewis Chemical Works. In 1997 Dr TI Rae edited Morison's manuscript for the Scottish Historical Journal and included his assessment of Donald Morison: 'Morison shows himself as a man of forthright judgement, a stern critic of ineptitude and of an independent turn of mind. He respected those whom he regarded as social superiors only if they merited that respect – and he had very little for Henry Caunter.' His working and personal relationship with Henry at the time of the Lewis Chemical Works however, was good; he even named one of his sons Henry Caunter Morison.

The manuscript was written twenty years after the Lewis Chemical Works ceased operations and four years before his death, but Morison's recollections are remarkably clear despite containing the odd factual error and misconception. Amongst the writings there are a number of coloured line drawings; plans and elevations of various parts of the apparatus – kilns, condensers, scrubbers, lime-kilns, etc – and ground plans. The accuracy of the ground plan for the main Creed site is confirmed by a simple survey of the site of the works using a few extant points of reference and by comparison to a large-scale aerial photo of the area. The detail of the line drawings allows a clear understanding of the chemical engineering principles involved in the distillation process. As the builder of the works Morison would have had ground plans and working plans which he probably kept. He also had copies of Paul's scientific papers. Post-Paul he appears to be the sole recorder of events as witnessed at the works.

Being a stone-mason was not just a job; Donald Morison was interested in the natural world. When he lived at the magnificent, turreted Creed Lodge at the entrance to the Lews Castle Grounds, 200 metres or so from the works, the inquisitive Donald managed to locate and dig up a thirteen pound meteorite which had fallen to earth near the lodge, placing it at his back door. The meteorite was still there when a descendant visited the island in the 1960s but has since disappeared.

Morison's personal qualities, abilities and interest in science would have appealed to the quixotic, mercurial but technically challenged Dr Benjamin Horatio Paul, an analytical chemist whose star was in the ascendancy and who, in 1858, had left London to take up the position of managing partner of the Lewis Chemical Works.

Chapter Three

Dr Benjamin Horatio Paul, Analytical Chemist

'... Cast in the heroic combative mould with
elements of sweetness and light in composition.'
(Obit. notice, Journal of the Chemical Society, 1918)

Benjamin Horatio Paul was born on the 6th August 1827
in the village of Snettisham in Norfolk, on the eastern shores
of the Wash. Throughout his youth his ambition was to be
a chemist and he was set down the path of his dreams by
a clerical relative who, in 1841, found the fourteen year old
Benjamin a position with Mr Cory, a chemist and druggist
in the nearby Norfolk town of Fakenham. The following
year the young Benjamin affirmed his position in life by
making his first professional mark; he joined the
Pharmaceutical Society. After a couple of years with Mr
Cory, Paul became disappointed with grinding mortars and
pestles and mixing lotions and potions; his active brain was
anxious to be stretched and he longed for the study of
chemistry.

So, in 1844, Paul left Fakenham and headed south to London to study his chosen subject, chemistry, at the school of the Pharmaceutical Society in their newly opened chemical laboratory, one of the first teaching laboratories in the country for the study of chemistry. Here he thrived and, immersed in the subject, he gained first prize in chemistry the following year. This earned Paul entry to the prestigious teaching laboratory at the University of Giessen, in Germany, the first such in the history of chemistry, situated in the country where major advances in the subject were being made. Paul was in a good place.

The teaching laboratory in Giessen had been founded by Justus von Liebig in 1824, when he had been appointed to the University of Giessen. Under his guidance the laboratory became *the* most influential centre for teaching chemistry. In 1845 Lord Kelvin was prompted to note: 'All the eminent chemists who were young in 1845 were pupils of Liebig.' If Paul was disappointed with his life just a few years earlier, when he stepped into the laboratory at Giessen he must have felt that, at last, he had arrived.

Liebig's method of teaching did not involve giving lectures or setting texts to be read, but depended on practical investigations. Liebig had a great gift of developing in his pupils the ability to carry these out. He was an excellent experimenter in his own studies but he was a poor demonstrator to others. This weakness mattered not to his pupils; if things did not work out as predicted, the keen chemist would want to know why and how his thinking went wrong. Negative results are always a positive in science.

Life at Giessen amongst like-minded and kindred spirits was idyllic. Liebig nurtured his students to look to themselves and to discover their own wisdom:

The progress of my special students depended on themselves. I gave the task and supervised. There was no instruction. Everyone was obliged to follow his own course. Disruption and amusement were not to be had at Giessen. How quietly we lived, except for scientific pursuits we have no excitements of the mind. We take walks in our beautiful green woods and in the evenings drink tea at the neighbouring old castles. This is our recreation.

Energy (and intellectual isolation) dictates that the social life of the student is always more robust than that of the teacher, as Carl Vogt, a student in 1834, recalls:

We who studied chemistry exclusively, formed a distinct clan at the University of Giessen. In the evening we dined, *en famille*, at the Black Horse Hotel whose keeper was a connoisseur in German white wines. This sociable evening meal led to sociable evening walks in summer and sociable drinking parties in winter. Thus we lived almost exclusively in a society of chemists.

Alas, there is no intimate knowledge of Paul's time at Giessen as records of that period were lost or misplaced during World War II. However it was while he was at Giessen in 1846 that Paul published his first scientific paper, at the grand age of nineteen, in the Pharmaceutical Journal, on the analysis of the metal cobalt. On 4th April 1848, Paul graduated from the University of Giessen with a PhD. While the degree of PhD is usually awarded for the presentation of a thesis on a particular topic, Paul's degree was awarded without him having to defend a thesis. In mid-nineteenth century Germany this was not unusual at the smaller universities. So Dr Paul returned to London armed with a degree in chemistry from the world's foremost chemistry institution, influential acquaintances in the expanding world of professional chemistry, and ambition. He was looking for a career.

Benjamin Paul had returned to London at the time when peat was very much in the news. The Irish Amelioration Society, under Roger's direction, had been established by Royal Charter and, a few months later, the scientific and political worlds were to be in the limelight when the O'Gorman Mahon and Lord Ashley made their infamous declaration in the House of Commons as to the perceived potential of peat. In response to this, the eminent chemist Sir Robert Kane had been asked to prepare a report on the possibilities of peat distillation. On Liebig's recommendation, Kane invited the newly qualified Paul to be his assistant on the project and so Paul found himself in Dublin. Unfortunately for Paul, this opening into new research was soon closed as Kane's former assistant was able to return to his post. Kane's assistant had been forced to flee Ireland after becoming involved in the political agitation of the day but was able to make a return after the influential intervention of Kane.

Paul stayed on in Ireland and was a frequent visitor to Kane's house. Kane was a giant in the world of science, especially chemistry, and Paul met many of the important scientists of the day. Paul was described as 'a brilliant conversationalist, an artistic raconteur of remarkable histrionic power with a wonderful gift of playful wit.' In short, the sort of person people would warm to and remember.

One of the scientists to take to him was Dr Thomas Andrews of Queen's College, Belfast, who is remembered for his pioneering work with carbon dioxide gas. Andrews invited Paul to help him at Queen's College, where a new chemistry laboratory was being built. Paul ended up staying in Ireland until 1850. He was in close contact with those involved in researching peat distillation even if he was not directly involved, and he would have seen any potential in peat as it was being realised.

In 1850, with a living to earn, Paul returned to London and worked for several years as an assistant to Dr Thomas Graham, who was the assayer to the Royal Mint and the Bank of England, where Paul conducted the assay business. Again, Paul had fallen into inspiring company; Graham was another of the chemistry greats of the time, discovering colloids and the laws of gas diffusion. Graham was also the first elected President of the Chemical Society when it was formed in 1841. However, after a few years of carrying out routine analyses, it was time for Paul to move on. He was asked to continue the job when Professor August Hofmann was appointed as successor to Graham in 1857, but Paul declined the invitation.

Paul had notions other than working for other people. His time on the continent had allowed him to develop as a skilled linguist and it was to translating from German and French that he turned to help his income, combining this facility with his love of science. Access to chemistry literature – both to research papers and to new textbooks – was not easy in the 1840s. The interests of the academic and industrial chemists were catered for by increasingly fragmenting societies. The Chemical Society and the Royal Institute of Chemistry were developing alongside the established Society of Arts.

This was the time of subscription societies, which were in effect small publishing houses aiming to produce specialist books that mainstream publishers would not touch; books with limited appeal but a guaranteed customer base. The Cavendish Society was one such, set up in 1846 to cover strictly chemistry-related subjects, especially for translating popular German works which, as WH Brock suggested, 'provided employment for needy men of science.'

On the encouragement of its founder members, Paul became a Fellow of the Cavendish Society and, in 1852, he passed the Major Exam of the School of Pharmacy (certificate number nine). He signed himself FCS in his translation of Alexander von Humboldt's *Cosmos: Sketch of a Physical Description of the Universe* published in the Bohn Scientific Library series. (He was also elected a Fellow of the Chemical Society – also FCS – but not until 1868.)

It was around 1852 that he began a translation of Gustav Bischoff's *Elements of Chemical and Physical Geology*, a substantial work of 1,500 pages. The Cavendish Society published volume one in 1854, volume two in 1855, and volume three in 1859. In 1857, Bohn published Paul's translation – altered and adapted – of the *Manual of Chemical Analysis applied to the Arts* by Dr PA Bolley of the University of Arau. This met with the full approval of the author: 'The very essential alterations in the arrangement and contents of the book were soon evident to me. I consider them much to its advantage and perceive from the general treatment of the subject that the book has fallen into just the right hands to be presented to English readers in an appropriate manner.'

The book was well-received by the press. The Examiner reviewed the tome as 'an important introduction to the use of chemistry in trade, well-adapted to the comprehension of the manufacturer who may learn how to perform his process. Dr Paul's work has been done skilfully.'

The volumes were a development of his youthful interest in chemical analysis; an interest which would grow. The title was aimed, not so much at the academic world, as at the development of chemistry in the commercial world,

114

which was not well-served by the chemical literature. Paul said of the Bolley translation: 'There are many well-defined lines of analytical enquiry which may be advantageously pursued by persons engaged in business who may be unable to avail themselves of the very scanty means that exist in this country of acquiring really practical and useful scientific knowledge.'

Had he read them, such sentiments would have given Matheson hope and heart at Henry Caunter's inability to proceed further with purifying the peat tar.

Paul was making his mark, becoming a leading light in spreading the written word of chemistry. In 1856, he had started a series of monthly publications in the Journal of the Pharmaceutical Society entitled 'Report of the Results of Physical and Chemical Investigations, and of the Applications of Physics and Chemistry in the Arts'. He was keeping one foot in the academic world and the other firmly in the industrial. These articles, described as 'successful' and 'accurate', continued monthly until July 1859 when he concluded with an article on the Distillation of Peat, published as he left London to become Managing Partner of the Lewis Chemical Works, there to develop the commercial possibilities of peat distillation on the island.

After encouraging others to bite the bullet of industrial chemistry, perhaps it was time for Paul to gain some practical experience for himself and, if things worked out, he stood to make a tidy sum and to enhance his growing reputation.

How Paul was engaged by Matheson is not known but the two men had mutual acquaintances who understood the needs of both. In 1860, Sir Roderick Murchison, James Matheson's scientific pal, made his last geological field trip to Lewis, sailing over with Matheson and his wife and enjoying a few days hunting and fishing on the estate while working on his rocks. In his detailed report to the Geological

Society describing his findings, Murchison makes specific reference to 'the Chemical Works at Garrabost under the direction of Mr Paul', a reference unrelated to the contents of the paper. Was this a nod of recognition to Paul? Sir Robert Kane – who was well aware of Paul's potential – along with Matheson and Murchison was a Fellow of the Royal Society. Murchison and Kane were both members of the Athæneum Club in London's Pall Mall, the haunt of society's scientists who would relax there after meetings and lectures to take dinner and to talk and gossip. It is easy to imagine a private dinner party at the Athæneum Club with Murchison and his guest Matheson, Kane and his guest Paul where the articulate, engaging and knowledgeable young man would be lured to the north by Matheson's promises of opportunity and fortune. At any rate, by early 1858 Paul was in Lewis.

James Matheson had secured a formidable force to help Henry Caunter. Paul could be abrasive; he was sarcastic and direct and didn't suffer fools, but he was also courteous, generous and likeable. How would Henry, the enthusiastic amateur scientist, take to Paul and the recently appointed Donald Morison who were both very good at what they did? Time would tell.

Paul was not just the blinkered scientist of the laboratory and the lecture theatre; there was more to him than books, test tubes of smelly liquids and the company of like-minds. In 1851, after he moved to London from Ireland, Paul stayed in lodgings in Westminster where was befriended by James Hannay, a journalist and native of Dumfries. Hannay – the same age as Paul – was to introduce him to a world outside his familiar science; to a way of life and a society in complete contrast to that of ordered and sheltered academia. Paul was about to break loose.

Hannay was an outrageous extrovert who, when Paul first met him, led a chaotic, Bohemian lifestyle. However, by the time of his alcohol-induced early death at the age of forty-six, whilst serving as British Consul in Barcelona, he was described as 'one of the most brilliant men of letters of the time.'

After an early discharge from the Royal Navy at just seventeen years of age, Hannay took to writing successful novels about life in the navy, contributing to comic magazines, and had spells as a journalist at the Morning Chronicle. By the time Paul met him, Hannay was writing satirical sketches for Punch magazine, but was constantly in debt, according to his biographer: 'He used to go out before the people were up and go home when they were in bed and he never apparently ate at all. He exchanged one set of lodgings for another seven times between 1850 and 1852.'

The man with the 'inexhaustible spirit' added Paul to his 'set'. Joseph Crowe, another of this 'set' recalls their lifestyle:

> In the evening, he [Hannay] would sally forth with as many congenial spirits as he could muster, drink drinks at the bars of public houses, make speeches at debating clubs and end up at midnight by knocking on the doors of a railway station and ordering a special train to take him to Dover; or he would get his friends together and tail on at the pit entrance of Drury Lane, and pelt the foremost rows of people from behind with oranges; then after witnessing half the performance, rise in the pit and describe the piece as rubbish and get turned out by a friendly policeman.

The gentle scientific society of Germany and Ireland were giving way to alcohol-fuelled revelry in the flesh-pots of Bohemian London. Liebig's 'disruptions, amusements and excitements of the mind' were taking on a new meaning as Paul's mind broadened.

Through Hannay, Paul met members of the Pre-Raphaelite Brotherhood (PRB); that group of rebellious young artists and writers who sought to express themselves by recording nature as they saw it, unadorned and unbound by any conventional rules. Paul made lasting friendships with the artist William Holman Hunt and with George Lewes, the philosopher, literary critic and partner of George Elliot. He became particularly close to William Michael Rossetti, the brother of Dante Gabriel Rossetti, the artist and poet and Christina Rossetti, the poet. They probably provided a respite from the whirlwind that was Hannay, as William Michael Rossetti describes;

> The PRBs were all high-thinking young men, assuredly not exempt from the infirmities of human nature, but bent upon working up to a true ideal in art and marked by habits generally abstemious rather than otherwise. To deny themselves the good things in life when forthcoming was not their notion, but, having next to no money to spend, they stuck to necessities and eschewed superfluities ... The Hannay set were equally impecunious but not equally abstemious. They also may have laid out little money, having laid in still less, but they breathed the atmosphere of 'devil-may-care' and were minded to jollify as best they could.

William Rossetti described the young Paul of 1851: 'Mr Paul was an agreeable companion, well-informed on a variety of subjects and not addicted to fads.'

Although he enjoyed outrageous company, Paul also liked

his fun to be serious. In 1854, Paul and William Rossetti went on holiday together to the south-west of England, a holiday which William, according to his brother Dante Gabriel, had 'journeyed, enjoying it vastly.' Forty years later, William Rossetti reminisced over that holiday: 'In 1854, I took a walking holiday with Mr Paul in Devon and Cornwall. We crossed Dartmoor on foot and got along (but not always on foot) to Land's End. We had a fine tramp the whole expedition.'

Besides his work in translating German science texts, in 1862 Paul was contracted, to translate *Memoirs of the Correspondence of Mallet du Pan*, a work on the French Revolution from the Royalist point of view. He received help from the Rossetti family, as William Rossetti recalled in 1895: 'Mr Benjamin Paul (a scientific chemist whom we knew in James Hannay's set) was the chief translator along with myself, and the female members of my family did something substantial.'

There is a suggestion in one of Paul's appreciations that Paul was very close to Dante Gabriel, that Paul was secretary of the PRB and that he and Dante Gabriel lodged together in Bloomsbury. This seems unlikely as William Michael acted as secretary of the PRB from its inception in the mid-1840s, and moreover, in the twelve volumes of the collected correspondence of Dante Gabriel Rossetti, there exists only one correspondence between the two; a brief note from Rossetti to Paul. This was an invitation to Paul, written in 1852, to come to a gathering at Rossetti's place to party with, amongst others, James Hannay. Rossetti playfully addresses Paul in Greek as 'Dear Παμλοξ' – literally 'Dear Paulos', Paulos being a Greek translation for Paul – flattering Paul's facility with languages.

Paul would still talk about his Bohemian friends in his twilight years; the period had left a deep impression on him, far more so than the four years he was to spend in Lewis.

Apart from the paper on the Lewis Chemical Works that he delivered to the Society of Arts and the British Association for the Advancement of Science after he left Lewis in 1862, Paul made no mention in his later writings, nor was any made in his obituaries, or appreciations written when he was still alive, of the Lewis Chemical Works and the four years he spent working in the Hebrides. Something in Lewis was to leave such an impression on him that he wished to forget his times in the north.

Chapter Four

Dr Paul has a Cunning Plan

'Paraffin is a material new to commerce
on a large scale'
– Sir Robert Kane

It was in the spring of 1858 when Benjamin Paul first became involved in what was to be the Lewis Chemical Works, when he was consulted as to the possibilities of working up the tar produced by Henry Caunter. By the time Paul arrived in Stornoway, Henry Caunter was living in Glen House, on what is still referred to as 'Caunter's corner'. The still extant house was occupied until a few years ago and is now undergoing renovation by a local businessman. The single-storey laboratory extension built by Donald Morison is still a major feature of the property, built to welcome Paul to a place where he could carry out his analyses in comfort, in close proximity to Caunter's fledgling works a mile down the road.

Paul set about his work, applying his incisive mind with systematic rigour. He was under no illusions as to the difficulty of the task in which he had become involved: 'The application of peat to some useful purposes has given rise to very sanguine, and I may say, in some cases, very exaggerated expectations and as a natural consequence it has been the source of disproportionate disappointment.'

He was, of course, referring to the O'Gorman Mahon fiasco of 1849. Although he had carefully studied Kane's Parliamentary Report of 1851 into peat distillation Paul would make his own practical investigations, paying close heed to Kane's conclusions regarding the cost of the purification of the raw materials, i.e. the peat and the tar.

There was to be one important commercially significant difference between Paul's proposed works on Lewis and the Irish peat works. Paul had noticed Kane's observation on the importance of paraffin as a product of peat distillation: 'It [paraffin] is a product new to commerce on a large scale and its value is not determined by comparative economy.' This observation had been made only seven years previously and much had happened to paraffin production during that time, especially in the central lowlands of Scotland, where James Young was at work with shale oil. Perhaps Paul was remembering his days in Ireland and visits to Kane's house, where peat distillation would have eagerly been discussed as Kane carried out his research.

Kane's report had noted that profit from the distillation of Irish peat must rely on other products besides paraffin, such as ammonium sulphate, calcium acetate and naphtha. There were good commercial markets for these products but a plentiful, cheap supply of the substances could be obtained from coal distillation carried out at common gas works. To try to produce them from peat in Lewis – as in Ireland – at a competitive price would seriously distort Paul's commercial thinking:

> A close examination of the subject of peat-working from a commercial point of view, led me to the conclusion that it is a fallacy to regard the products [ammonium sulphate etc] as a source of profit to be obtained in working peat. On the contrary, I consider that no reliance should be placed on the value of these products as contributing in any way towards the possibility of peat being worked advantageously ... the question of whether peat can be worked remuneratively must be determined by regarding the oils and paraffin alone as the staple products.

Paul had carefully analysed the 1855 report to the directors of the Irish Peat Company which showed a staggering difference between the expected profit, as set out in Rees Reece's prospectus of 1851, and the actual profit obtained: 'Instead of being worth £12,700 a year, [the products] were worth only £1,752 according to the company's own returns; and they probably cost more than that sum to manufacture.'

The cost of the peat in Ireland had been far more than anticipated and the product quantities produced were very disappointing. The production of paraffin oil for burning in lamps had not actually been attempted due to its offensive smell, unlike the sweet-smelling oil subsequently obtained from Lewis peat.

Here was an opportunity, if paraffin could be produced at the right price, to cash in on a new commodity and at the same time realise Matheson's hopes for the people of Lewis. Paul said that Lewis peat was:

> a means of establishing a productive industry and also of affording what is so much needed there – a greater opportunity for employment

– while at the same time the condition of the people would be bettered: and, by the removal of the peat, the land would be cleared for cultivation ... and rendered less unfavourable to vegetation. At present, however, the peat deposits of these islands ... though containing the elements of social amelioration, of industry and of wealth, lie like a huge inanimate chaos, burying the land which might yield abundant harvests, preventing the labour of the inhabitants and hindering the development and maturing of the crops on those few patches of ground which are yet cultivated.

Paul was motivated. Using standard analytical procedures, he set to work on the tar produced by Caunter and managed to isolate two oils. The first oil or paraffin was:

of a pale yellow colour with a slight and not unpleasant smell. It burned well in the lamps commonly used for hydrocarbon [i.e. paraffin] oils, with a brilliant white flame. Its boiling point being [high] there was no danger of its giving off explosive vapour at any temperature it would likely to be heated to when used in a lamp as compared with some other oils.

The second oil Paul describes as being 'of a pale yellow colour and scarcely any smell ... when mixed with fat oils it formed an excellent lubricator.'

Paul's initial analyses were encouraging, so he proceeded to consider the practical arrangements for distilling the peat to produce tar. Distillation involves two stages: the first is the heating of the peat to form a vapour or gas and the second is the condensing of these hot vapours – cooling them down – to form liquid tar.

As mentioned earlier, there were two types of apparatus for heating the peat (see diagram in plate section). In the 'closed' method, the peat was placed in a retort and heated from the outside using more peat. The drawback of using a retort was that it had to be allowed to cool once all the tar had been produced, so that it could be emptied and recharged with a fresh batch of peat. The solid remains of the peat – charcoal – was an excellent fuel in its own right. In the 'open' method the peat was heated in a kiln. Here, the container, or kiln, was open at both ends and set vertically. The peat in the kiln was set on fire at its base where air was supplied. The heat from this burning peat rose through the bulk of the peat, which started to distil, producing a vapour. As the burning peat at the base of the kiln turned to ash, the distilled peat above – which had turned to charcoal – acted as fuel to heat the fresh peat added to the kiln, making the process continuous. The downside to using a kiln was that it was more difficult for the operator to control.

The other major piece of apparatus that Paul needed to consider was the condenser, used to cool the vapour, converting it to a liquid and separating it from peat gas. Condensers commonly used in gas works were usually just long lengths of pipe, connected in a series by metal or wooden boxes and kept cool by the surrounding air or by a bath or spray of water. Condenser and kiln/retort design were key to the efficient production of tar from peat.

To obtain the paraffin from the tar required the tar itself to be distilled using a separate retort and condenser along with treatment by various chemicals, notably sulphuric acid. Using this apparatus, known as a refinery, the tar could be separated into so-called light oil, heavy oil, paraffin – liquid, solid wax and creosote. (The same process occurs today in an oil refinery e.g. at Grangemouth, where crude oil from the North Sea is separated into petrol, diesel, paraffin, fuel oil etc.)

Paul's initial analyses were made on tar produced by Caunter using an open kiln. Paul wanted to compare the amount of tar produced (the yield) with that produced using a closed retort. So he altered and rebuilt Caunter's kiln, fashioning it into a retort. Henry was not pleased, as Morison reports: 'Mr Caunter and Wilson's apparatus was quite upset by Dr Paul, to the great greaf of the enventors.'

The results showed the retort to give the greater yield of tar, just as Kane had discovered in Ireland. Further analysis of the two tars from the kiln and the furnace showed them to be quite different with respect to the proportions of light oils, heavy oils and paraffin. Paul's explanation was to blame poor Henry's condenser: 'The difference might, however, be owing to defective condensation ... as the arrangements [condenser] connected with the experimental [Caunter's] kiln were in many respects very imperfect.'

Disappointingly, Paul discovered that the yield of paraffin from the Lewis tar was considerably less than that produced by Kane from the Irish tar. Paul was not discouraged; he reasoned that this was the result of the difference in the peat in the two countries, brought about by their different methods of formation.

The peat in Ireland is known as 'bog' or 'raised' peat and was originally formed on marshes or lakes which provided the necessary water-logged conditions. These conditions produced very deep peat – anything up to a hundred feet – but a peat of low quality when used for fuel. By contrast, the vast majority of Lewis peat is of a type known as 'mountain' or 'blanket' peat and covers the whole terrain, hilltops as well as valleys (although small patches of raised peat do exist in Lewis, for example an area of land lying between Loch Suirstavat and Little Loch Roag in the Uig district). The water-logged conditions in this case are the result of high rainfall rather than ground water. This mountain peat forms in much thinner layers than the bog peat – typically from two to ten feet – but the quality of the peat as a fuel is far superior. It is denser and less fibrous, producing the dark brown/black fuel of the Lewis peat stack. This mountain peat burns with a good flame which has been accurately described as 'not too hot and not too cool.'

The fact that even the dry peat contains about 20% water actually increases the heat it gives out when burned. At high temperature and in the presence of glowing charcoal, the water is broken up to release hydrogen gas which is itself a very efficient, hot-burning fuel. The characteristic almost colourless, dancing flame associated with burning hydrogen can occasionally be seen floating above burning peat, especially in a glass-fronted stove, when the conditions are right.

So Paul put his ideas to the test. Using a retort, he first measured the yield of tar from peat and found that the Lewis peat gave over four times as much tar as the Irish. He next measured the yield of paraffin obtained from the tar, only to discover that the Lewis peat tar gave just over half that obtained from the Irish peat tar. However, by combining these two sets of results it became apparent that the overall yield of paraffin from peat was much greater for the Lewis mountain peat. Paul neatly summarised his analyses in the following table.

	Tons	Tar (gallons)	Refined oil; paraffin (gallons)
Lews peat	100	2,097	999
Irish peat	100	478	357

His completed chemical analysis allowed Paul to consider practical matters: a kiln or a retort. Paul chose to use a kiln although it gave a lower yield (by 14%) of tar:

At the onset of the inquiry into the working of the Lews peat it became an important question whether it would not be more economical to work with kilns as was done in the Irish works; whether the large yield of tar obtained with retorts was not to some extent only apparent; and whether a smaller yield of tar obtained by means of kilns, might be more advantageous by reason of the smaller original cost and of their requiring a smaller expense for labour and fuel in working than retorts.

Having opted for kilns, Paul addressed the method to be used for firing the peat. The Irish works had used an air-blast from a pump, blown through the kiln. Kane did not think much of the blast machine, describing it as 'very inefficient and producing an intermittent blast of no great power.'

Using data from Dr Hodges – a co-worker of Rees Reece, the original patentee of the blast method and with whom Paul had worked when living in Ireland – Paul showed that the blast pump was an expensive piece of kit which actually hindered the removal of tar from the kiln where it would be destroyed by burning. Paul opted instead for having a grate at the base of the kiln to raise the burning peat and help the entry of air. The draught through the kiln was to be created by use of a chimney, most likely at Henry Caunter's suggestion: 'This option was supported by the results of some experiments made with a small kiln constructed in this manner which was worked for some time in Lews [Caunter's kiln]. In this kiln the draught was produced by means of a chimney placed at the further end of the condenser.' Henry's pride would no doubt have been given a boost by the use of his engineering design.

The chemical analyses and practical considerations were all very promising but Paul needed to carry out a full economical analysis to see if the chemistry could become a commercial reality. In Ireland, the depth of the peat required the cut peat to be moved by barrow from the cutting surface to the drying grounds, where it was placed either on racks or on dry ground if available. This required considerable man power, especially when handling the deeper, higher quality peat. In Lewis, Paul observed how the peat banks were opened up by cutting a trench about three feet wide and exploiting the banks on either side of this trench, the peat being thrown directly from the cutting iron onto the ground where it was to dry: 'The advantage of this method of cutting is that there is no necessity of removing the peat by barrows to the spreading ground, a procedure which is attended by considerable expense of labour.'

Although Paul saw the method of cutting Lewis peat as advantageous, he was conscious of the major disadvantage of using peat as a raw material; that of gathering and transporting the dried peat to the factory: 'The extent to which this disadvantage affects any particular instance of the use of peat will depend very much on the skill exercised in laying out the grounds for cutting the peat and in disposing the banks and tram roads, or other means, for carrying the peat to the place where it is to be used.' The reference to 'other means' was a possible nod to Caunter's ingenious canal for delivery of the peats across the moorland. However Paul was to produce an elegant solution of his own to solve the peat delivery problem.

As to the important factors of favourable cutting weather and the availability of a good work force, Paul was quite confident: 'As a rule it might be said that the month of May is the only time available for cutting peat in the Hebrides, so as, on the one hand to avoid the destruction of peat by frost [when cut-peat becomes frozen and crumbles to a powder] and on the other hand to ensure the best possible chance to getting it well dried.' No mention of midges! But Paul understood the working year of the crofter: 'The people are almost all fisherman and the fishing season does not commence until the end of May or June so it would be possible to obtain many of these men before they go to the fishing and so the inconvenience of employing a large number of men for a short period would not be so great there as it would be in most other instances.'

Paul had no doubts concerning the organisation of the hundreds of labourers envisaged. He was impressed by the Lewisman's ability to billet himself on the peat cutting ground:

> Moreover, these people are accustomed to hutting themselves, with no small degree of comfort, in huts or bothies built of the surface sods of the peat, and they live in these as a rule, throughout the Hebrides, so that a squad of 200 or 300 men may find, on the ground where they are going to work, the materials for their encampment and it is interesting to see the dexterity and quickness with which they construct these bothies.

Paul completed his consultation and assessment of peat, tar and crofters and produced a comprehensive commercial plan for a factory to produce paraffin from peat. He produced a costing for every stage of the process, from digging the peat to refining the tar with a competitive price for the paraffin of 1s 2½d (6p) per gallon. He used Caunter's actual costs for cutting, drying and stacking the peat and for producing tar as a starting point. Paul was led to believe that the cost of labour for producing the dried peat could be substantially reduced from Caunter's contract price: 'At the time [of Caunter's works] the cost of peat on the moorland was 2s 6d (12½p) per ton for cutting, drying and stacking by contract, but there were satisfactory reasons for expecting that it could be obtained at a less expense.'

Paul was not misled; within three years the price was reduced to 1s 6d (7½p). Could this have been Matheson's factor, Donald Munro, using his threatening tactics on the labourers to gain some influence in this sphere of the estate life? Munro was known to interfere in the running of the works, especially when an accusatorial finger could be pointed at the crofters. Maybe he saw Caunter or Paul as a threat to his absolute power.

It had taken the best part of a year for Paul to produce his plan for Matheson's consideration but Matheson duly awarded him with a commission to superintend the planning and erection of a large works for the distillation of peat to produce paraffin in Lewis. The Lewis Chemical Works had become a fact of life. Paul took the position of 'managing partner' which seems to carry with it connotations of commercial return. Quite who his partner was is not known but most likely it was Matheson himself; he was the commissioner and he was paying the bills. Caunter also had a vested interest, but he is referred to by Donald Morison quite early on as simply 'the worthy paymaster.'

Paul was also given responsibility for overseeing the Garrabost Brick Works, where he was given a house in which to live and servants. This put him firmly in charge of all of Matheson's hopes for a continued scientific revolution on Lewis after the early disappointments of the Deanston venture, when William Smith had tried to reclaim moorland in central Lewis. On a personal level, Paul was no doubt keen to put into practice his ideas from his much heralded *Manual of Chemical Analysis applied to the Arts*, published the previous year. The Lewis Chemical Works was probably his first step into the world of practical industrial chemistry. He was swapping the test tube and Bunsen burner for large kilns and condensers and he was going to get his hands dirty.

Portrait of Sir James Matheson by
Daniel Macnee.
From the collections of
Museum nan Eilean

ABOVE Henry Caunter.
Reproduced courtesy of Ros Fletcher

LEFT Henry Caunter's grave in the
churchyard of St Peter's Episcopal
Church, Stornoway

Donald Morison.
Reproduced courtesy of
Bill Scott

Dr Benjamin Horatio Paul.
Museum of the Royal
Pharmaceutical Society

The Beginning and the End
of The Lewis Chemical Works,

The destillation of Hydro carbon
Oil from Peal in the Lewis
Island was first conceived by
Henry Caunter Esqr. a, retainor of
Sir James Mathison Baronet, and
Propritor of the Lewis Island
          Mr Caunter was, a
Gentleman of extensive Knowledge
and a sanguine temperment,
possessed with and ardent desire
to Therorise and experiment,
with the hope of making a
descovery hitherto unknown to
the arts and sciences
a, gifted speaker able to
Convince his hearers however

The first page of Donald Morison's manuscript.
Reproduced by permission of the National Library of Scotland

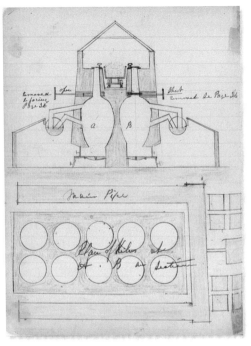

BELOW The north-facing elevation of the Creed Works compiled from illustrations in Donald Morison's manuscript.

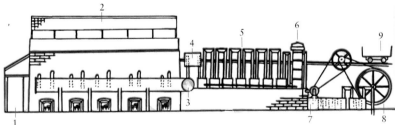

The north-facing elevation of the Creed works compiled from illustrations in Donald Morison's manuscript.

1 - lime store
2 - kiln house
3 - large cast iron pipe taking tar vapour to the condensers
4 - water joint safety valve
5 - condensers
6 - scrubber tower
7 - fan
8 - drive from steam engine
9 - tramway from the moor to deliver peat to the top of the kiln block

Advertisements from the Post Office Annual Glasgow directory
for 1867/8 showing the range of products available from the
Lewis Chemical Works. Reproduced by permission of the
National Library of Scotland

Aerial photograph of the Creed site looking north, showing
the extent of the peat workings. The works are at the centre
of the lower edge of the photo with the straight line of the
tramway bed clearly visible between the peat banks. Just to
the north lies the canal: the wharves can be seen as dark
areas on its southern bank. Beyond the meandering Paraffin
Burn lie more peat banks and tramway bed. To the south of
the main tramway flows the River Creed.

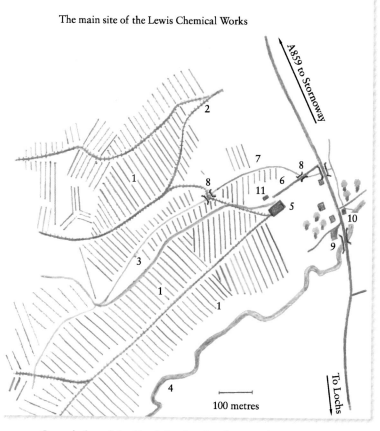

The main site of the Lewis Chemical Works

Ground plan of the Creed site showing the main features;

1 – Peat banks
2 – Tramway
3 – Canal
4 – River Creed
5 – Lewis Chemical Works factory site
6 – Cartway
7 – Paraffin Burn
8 – Bridges
9 – Car park with memorial plaque
10 – Creed Lodge
11 – Caunter's original works

The site of the Creed works looking west;

     1 – Caunter's original works
     2 – Paul's works
     3 – The line of the tramway to the tar pits
     4 – The cart way from the main road to Caunter's works
     5 – The Paraffin Burn flowing to the River Creed
     6 – The tar pits where the tar was allowed to cool

Glen House, Stornoway, where Henry Caunter
lived and worked, (left) approx. 1900 and (right) 2017

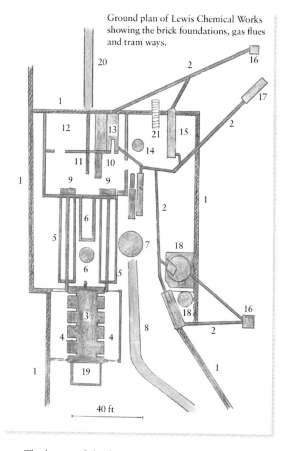

Ground plan of Lewis Chemical Works showing the brick foundations, gas flues and tram ways.

The layout of the factory site at the Creed works
(after Donald Morison);

1 – Retaining wall
2 – Gas flues
3 – Kilns
4 – Ash pits
5 – Seats for condensers
6 – Receiving and settling tanks
7 – Vat
8 – Tramway to tar pits
9 – Condensers
10 – Steam engine
11 – Drum for rope hauling machine
12 – Store
13 – Steam boiler
14 – Grease mill
15 – Lime furnace
16 – Stack
17 – Gas burner
18 – Evaporating boilers
19 – Lime store
20 – Tramway to peat banks
21 – Stair

Creed works tramway bed and peat workings looking west.

Peatbank

Creed works canal looking west.

Recycled tramway line used as a fence post at Maryhill near Stornoway.

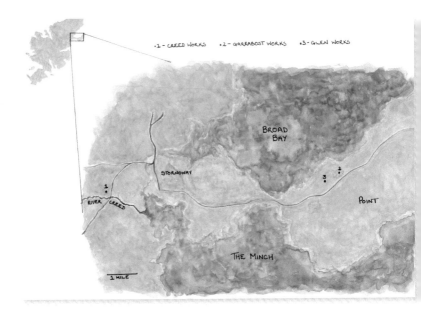

The separation of the three sites of the Lewis Chemical
Works.

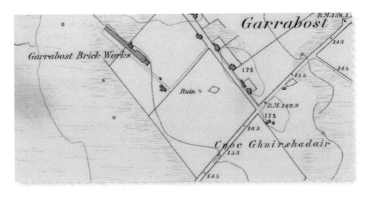

OS 6 inch map of Ross-shire (Isle of Lewis)
Sheet 21 published 1851, showing Garrabost Brickworks.
Reproduced by permission of the National Library
of Scotland.

The remains of the Garrabost brickworks, today used as a byre.

'An t-Seada Dheargh' (The Red Building) is all that remained of Garrabost brickworks in 1976 when this photo was taken. After the closure of the brickworks in the late 1880s the building was converted into a substantial dwelling house and latterly a byre. © © HES. Reproduced courtesy of J R Hume

The western gable wall has collapsed since 1976 and rebuilt further east in the building in order to try to preserve the remains. © © HES. Reproduced courtesy of J R Hume

The excavated tramway base between the Garrabost brickworks and the Knock stills showing the wooden sleepers still in place.

Site of the glen stills at Knock.

Condenser/scrubber tower cap at the Knock site.

Iron plate set into the floor of the kiln house at the
Garrabost mill, thought to be the bed of a steam engine.

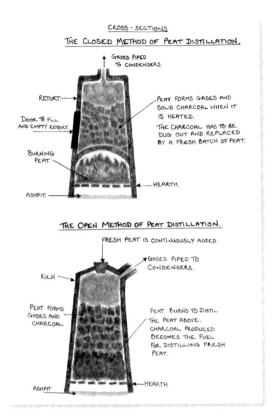

CROSS - SECTIONS

THE CLOSED METHOD OF PEAT DISTILLATION.

GASES PIPED
TO CONDENSERS.

RETORT.

DOOR TO FILL
AND EMPTY RETORT.

BURNING
PEAT.

ASHPIT.

PEAT FORMS GASES AND
SOLID CHARCOAL WHEN IT
IS HEATED.

THE CHARCOAL HAS TO BE
DUG OUT AND REPLACED
BY A FRESH BATCH OF PEAT.

HEARTH.

THE OPEN METHOD OF PEAT DISTILLATION.

FRESH PEAT IS CONTINUOUSLY ADDED.

GASES PIPED TO
CONDENSERS.

KILN

PEAT FORMS
GASES AND
CHARCOAL

ASHPIT

PEAT BURNS TO DISTIL
THE PEAT ABOVE.
CHARCOAL PRODUCED
BECOMES THE FUEL
FOR DISTILLING FRESH
PEAT.

HEARTH

Open and closed methods of peat distillation.
After careful experimentation, Paul chose the open method.

This stone marks the site of
The Lewis Chemical Works,
set up by Sir James Matheson
to extract paraffin from peat.
1857 - 1874

Stone marking the site of the Lewis Chemical Works.

Chapter Five

Construction and Destruction

'The eminent Analyst and Chemist would be
more at Home among his Books and his
Laboratory than superintending the erection
of the Works'
– Donald Morison

Benjamin Paul had done his homework and so in the spring
of 1859 hopes were high, despite previous failures of peat
distillation in other parts of the country. Everything was in
place for him to put his commercial plans for paraffin
production into place. The peat distillation was to be carried
out on a new site, near Caunter's original works, close to
the River Creed just south of Stornoway. The refining of
the tar was to take place in Caunter's works until a new
refinery was completed.

According to Morison, Caunter and Paul made a trip to
Germany to visit a peat distillery before building started in
Lewis, a trip which appeared to have been fruitless:

> After a series of experiments, Dr Paul and Mr
> Caunter went to Germany to visit the only

peat works then in existence. All they saw at the German works was that empty Herring Barrels with the Stornoway brand did service as condensers, set and connected like Wolf's Bottles [a piece of chemical apparatus] with Wooden pipes, the gas escaping in all directions through the joints. The rest of the Works was in Keeping. So the trip to Germany at Sir James's expense was a failure as far as practical information for the Distillation of Peat was concerned.

Whether this report was just a result of Caunter blethering to Morison and letting his enthusiasm for the Lewis project affect his judgement is not known. It seems unlikely that German efficiency and knowledge at the time would lead to such a description. Germany would have been a fertile ground for making observations; for years peat charcoal had been produced by distillation across Europe for the iron-smelting industry and at Beul, on the Rhine, stood a manufactory for producing paraffin and oils from a local mineral – brown coal – which was operational from 1845 – 1863, and known to Paul. Paul made another trip to Germany alone, the following year, just before production started, perhaps to see his old mentor Liebig at Giessen.

In May 1859, construction started at the Creed Works, as they became known, where the kiln block was built out of Garrabost brick. Literally thousands of bricks would have been required for the structure which was located about thirty metres south of Caunter's works, in a slight depression on higher ground. The block containing the ten kilns was about forty feet by twenty feet and stood about twenty feet high with a tiled roof. At a conservative estimate this would have required a minimum of about 30,000 bricks, so the brickworks would have been working well. Paul described the kiln and condenser design in detail:

> The tar kilns were cylindrical brick chambers 5 feet diameter and 12 feet high, with a fire-grate of about 2 feet area at the lower end, and a hopper with a lid at the top for introducing the peat. Ten of these kilns were constructed side-by side in a block of brickwork [in two rows of five, back-to-back]. From the side of each kiln passed a pipe 12 inches in diameter which was connected with a main [a large pipe] three feet diameter extending around the whole range of kilns and into which the tar vapours from the kilns were discharged.

The condensers were very simple in design. Paul continued:

> From the main, the vapour passed in a series of pipes twelve inches diameter arranged on cisterns [boxes made of cast iron] much the same way as cisterns at a gas works but with the difference that there was no water joint. After passing through the condenser, the uncondensed gases were discharged into a brick chamber with numerous partition walls and thence into a large flue running about 50 yards up the side of a hill at the top of which was placed a chimney 50 feet high.

The design of the kilns was quite different from those of the Irish Peat Works – which was still operational – in number, size and construction. In Ireland there were four kilns arranged in a square, each six feet wide and sixteen feet high and made from brick, covered in riveted boiler plate for strength. They were fired by a hot-air blast from

135

a fan. Paul used a greater number of smaller kilns as he was concerned that a tall kiln would cause the tar to condense on the cool peat at the top of the kiln, melt and run down to the fire at the base and burn, so being destroyed.

By contrast, the design and dimensions of the remaining pipes in Paul's design was an exact copy of those in the Irish works. The only difference was the absence of water joints. Morison indicates that the height of the peat in the Irish kilns was thirty-two feet compared to twelve feet in Lewis. According to a technical description of the Irish works in Ure's Dictionary, although the *outside* height of the kilns is thirty-two feet, the peat column *inside* the kilns was only about sixteen feet.

The absence of water joints is astounding as it would have allowed inflammable gas from the kilns to mix with air in the condensers and create an explosive mixture which had direct contact with the very hot kilns. This absence was to have repercussions.

From the start of the construction, Morison knew what was expected of Paul and his design: 'No doubt Dr Paul realised the Fact that the first operation, That is to Erect a Work to extract the Crude Hydrocarbon etc [tar] from Peat was more a Practical and mechanical than Chemical operation.' As the work proceeded, Morison's curiosity at the apparent random siting of the works, became aroused: 'The killing of the Fish in the Pond and the difficulty of getting water was strongly overlooked in chusing a site, when there was such a Field to select from more suitable in many respects.' This curiosity soon developed into a healthy scepticism of Benjamin Paul's abilities as Morison concluded: 'It was quite evident during the erection of the works, That the eminent Analyst and Chemist would be more at Home among his Books and in his Laboratory than superintending the erection of the Works.'

There was a rational explanation for this apparent disregard for the need for water. Paul was sticking to his plan and producing an economical and ergonomical method of bringing the dried peat from the banks to the kiln mouth. Water could easily be raised by pumps and salmon were for eating rather than sport. His plan was to build a tramway to bring the peats from the moor. The tramway from the peat banks went directly across the top of, and between, the double row of kilns. Peat could be emptied straight into the kiln mouths from the trucks, or hutches as they were known, with little need for handling, making it a low-cost operation.

From the kilns, the tramway stretched fully three quarters of a mile out into the moor, down a very gentle slope near the crest of high ground. The occasional 'railway cutting' through the peat, a couple of feet deep, allowed the line to keep its gradient. About half a mile from the works the tramway diverged and a branch headed to the north to give access to further peat deposits. The peat banks were arranged at a slight angle to the tramway, following the line of drainage. The banks to the south of the line dipped down to the River Creed, while those to the north crossed near-horizontal moor which dipped slightly towards Caunter's canal. The aerial photograph of the area, taken in 1963, shows a herringbone appearance as the ribs of the peat banks run off the tramway spine, and the direct path of the line to the kilns is clear.

This arrangement of the peat banks provided a cheap, elegant system of peat delivery to the kilns. As the peats dried on the banks where they had been thrown, they were gathered towards the tramway end of the bank where they were loaded onto the hutches. These were man-handled up the gentle slope to arrive at the track-end on top of the kilns into which the peat was tipped. Later on a more sophisticated method was introduced with the installation of a steam-engine, which drove a cable drum to haul the trucks up the slope. The Lewis men gave this tramway a much grander title as the John O'Groat Journal correspondent noted in 1860: 'A tramway – the Lewis Railroad as it is jocularly termed – has been made from the manufactory down to a moss where extensive cuttings have already been made and where I witnessed a great number of men and women employed in casting the peats.'

Morison's daughter Mary-Jane's first-hand recollection of riding in wind-driven hutches fitted out with a mast and sail was passed to her grandson, Bill Scott, by his mother. This goes along with an oral tradition in Lewis which suggests that the crofters supplemented their own motive power with a little ingenuity. They knew how to live with, and harness, their harsh climate.

The line of the tramway and the layout of the peat banks are still very evident today and these features become very enhanced on the vertical aerial photo of the area. The tramway was quite a piece of civil engineering – probably built with Messrs Wilson, Caunter and Morison supplying the guiding thought. The build method was revealed during the recent archaeological Watching Brief. An exploratory trench was dug across the line of the tramway which indicated that the same logical approach to its construction – reading the lie of the land – had been taken as with the canal. The straight line of the tramway was bordered with low banks which varied in height according to the topography. Archaeologist Carol Knott revealed that the foundation of the tramway was effectively the bedrock, Lewisian Gneiss, which is near to the surface on the ridge of the land. The up-cast material – stone, clay, turfs, and gritty peat – from bedding the track formed a shallow bank on either side of the track bed. The bank to the north of the tramway had been laid on undisturbed peat but that to the south directly onto the bedrock. Nothing was left to chance; ground water was carefully controlled by gutters, small shallow drains about five inches deep, cut into the hard gneiss on either side of the track.

After nearly a century and a half without use, the foundation of the tramway is now covered in a couple of feet of peaty silt as the moor reclaims its covering. The peat banks now appear as mere undulations on the surface of the otherwise flat moorland, as the pattern appears to stretch endlessly to the horizon. A miserable place in awful weather for the labourers but at least it meant pennies at the end of the day. A correspondent from the Inverness Courier visiting the works in 1865 reported that: 'About four to five hundred pounds a year is paid to work-people for cutting and securing these peats; there being about 800 irons of them cut at 11s 6d (57½p) the iron. An iron of peats is what a peat iron will cut in one day, when kept going all day and when it is expected to have at least to cut seventy-five yards of solid peat moss.' Eight hundred irons at 75 yards to the iron equates to about thirty-five miles of peat banks.

The aerial survey of 1963 allows an estimate to be made of the amount of peat cut. The individual peat banks are clearly visible and some 300 or so are easily counted. The length of the banks vary, but taking an average length of 150 yards, a conservative estimate would indicate the remains of about thirty to thirty-five miles of peat banks, agreeing with the 1865 report. This is a staggering figure when considering that a single household would probably cut about 100 yards of bank for a year's supply of fuel. No wonder Paul was counting his work force of cutters in the hundreds.

As the works progressed, the tramways were further developed to the north of Caunter's canal, until about three and a half miles had been laid. This involved the building of a bridge to cross the Paraffin Burn and the construction of embankments. The survey indicates that the embankments were made from a mixture of thrown-up peat and dried peat dross. Regular drainage channels through the embankment were probably crossed by wooden trestles supporting the tramway.

By this time the total length of the peat banks was a back-breaking fifty miles or so. Whether all the peat banks were worked at the same time is not known, but at its peak the works was distilling about one hundred tons of peat per week. From the regular spacing of the banks, they do not appear to have been exhausted of fuel, nor had they been abandoned and replaced by new banks.

All that remains of the tramway, other than its impression on the landscape, are short sections of the rail itself, which, when the works closed down, was lifted and used by the crofters as fence posts. For this, the rail was cut into short, six foot lengths and two eyelets added, about a foot apart, one foot from one end, through which a strand of fence-wire could be drawn. Some posts can still be seen standing in the Marybank district of Stornoway, alongside stone dykes. At the site of the tar pits, near the stream just east of the works – the tar was cooled and stored before being carted to Garrabost for refining – a ten foot length of rail was still visible until about forty years ago but has since 'sunk without trace'.

Unlike modern railway tracks, the rails were laid on lengthwise wooden sleepers which were tied at intervals with cross-sleepers. The gauge is not known. The rails were held down by nails driven through holes punched through the base of the rails which caused the metal to splay. The rail was of a design known as 'bridge' rail on account of its shape in cross section which resembles a flat-topped hump-back bridge. Not having to bear a great weight, the rails are quite light, the base being about two and a half inches wide and the height about one and a half inches. This design shape was also known as a 'Brunel' rail; so called after the great 19th century engineer, Isambard Kingdom Brunel, who developed a larger version of that design of rail for his seven-foot gauge Great Western Railway.

By September of 1859, the kiln block had been completed and work had started on the condensers. The construction of the condenser base again required a large number of bricks to be produced. The brick makers were never idle – yet. The condensers proved troublesome, the problem being that, although Paul knew what he was trying to do, he did not know how to achieve it, as Morison pointed out: 'The absence of a Definite Plan for the Work from first caused delays and expensive alterations while the work was being fitted up for the first trial.'

Leaving Caunter in charge, Paul went off to Germany again in the summer of 1860 while work on the condensers continued. Hopes for the future were high as the John O'Groat Journal reporter informed readers in August 1860, after interviewing Henry Caunter: 'The promoters are very sanguine of success and, if successful, the manufacture will prove a permanent source of employment to a considerable number of the natives, the chief object.' Is there just a hint of caution reported here however?

By September 1860, all was ready for the blue touch-paper to be lit. Once the kilns had been fired up and running for a short period, troubles immediately became apparent. The kiln-block design and orientation, with its two rows of kilns built back to back, had a basic flaw concerning the draw of the flues. Paul had omitted to consider the one important, over-riding factor concerning the control of fire in Lewis – the wind! Morison summarised the problem succinctly:

'The Windward side [of the kiln block] burnt so fiercely that the furnace bars bent down to the Ashpits while the Lee side spewed out Volumes of smoke.'

Paul's condensers also proved a major disappointment as 'it was found that the Brick Flew [sic] Connecting the Funnel with the Condensers produced More Peat Tar than the whole range of condensers which produced little more than Brown Water, and during Snow a Brown track of Tar could be seen fully half mile to the Lee of the Funnel.' The tar was not condensing in the condensers but was being exhausted from the iron chimney on the hill.

The poor kiln operators' job was thoroughly unpleasant, especially during periods of calm weather. Each kiln had to be charged with fresh peat every two or three hours. This involved opening the mouth of the kiln which allowed the tarry gas to escape. It is in the nature of smelly gases that their smell becomes more apparent at great dilution and that the character of the smell changes. The tantalising, sweet smell of peat-reek, sensed miles from its source, becomes an eye-watering antiseptic nearer its flame, and closer still a foul-smelling, choking gas, best avoided (as anyone who has had a chimney blow-down will testify). For the kiln operator there was no escape:

> Particularly in Calm Weather when charging the Kilns with Peat. A fresh relay of Men in the open Air ready to haul out any that would succumb, take him round with Bukets of Water on his Face and head. On one occation, Dr Paul being present, Three Men were hauled out to the open Air remained striched on their back in a delirious state for several hours. The after-effects disabling them from Work for two days.

It was hard graft. Paul was disappointed but spent a week and a half making alterations. By early October 1860 the works were fired up again, but with a different kindling technique. Paul left the works with instructions for the kilns to be lit two at a time on alternate sides until they were all aflame. The effect of this – unforeseen by anyone – was that after half the kilns had been lit, the works were effectively a time-bomb. The lit kilns produced the highly inflammable gas while the unlit kilns allowed the entry of fresh air. The two gases mixed and so a highly explosive gas filled the condensers which, in the absence of the water joints, was directly connected to the flame and heat of the burning peat. There was only one possible outcome as Morison described:

> The result of the Manner of Kindling the Furnaces were, that an hour after Dr Paul left the Works a Fearful explosion took place, smashing several of the Cast Metal Tanks to pieces, scattering the Galvanised pipes and crossends in all directions, shaking the Earth and Causing the Dishes in the nearest House (460 yards distant) to rattle on the table [probably Morison's own cottage]. In Stornoway it was thought to THUNDER. Nothing less than a Miracle saved the Men on duty.

Paul was immediately recalled to the works to find that his meticulous planning of the last eighteen months lay in ruins. He was 'put about'! But 'when Firmlay told by his Foreman [Donald Morison] that his orders was strickley being carried out in kindling the Kilns, he ceased to lay the blame on the Men, Admitted it was an overlook of his.'

The explosion soon reached the ears of Donald Munro, Matheson's factor, who waded straight in to have a go at the workforce. Munro was soon brought down to earth by

Donald Morison who in his diplomatic manner deferred to his superior, defended his men and set things to right:

> Soon after Donald Munro, Sir James's Factor Came to the works, Expressed the hope that we would attend to Messrs Paul and Caunter's directions in future and not Explode and smash the works again by not attending to orders. This only shows how Gen[tlemen] make skape Goats of those under them. By Mr Munro's knowledge of Cross questioning he left the works with the real Cause of the Explosion etc, or rather the knowledge that the orders for kindling was strickley adhered to.

Unbowed, Paul approached the catastrophe as if it was just another logistical problem. Tradesmen were brought in to replace the smashed cast-iron boxes with cheaper wooden ones and just over a week later, in mid-October, the kilns were again ready to be lit. This time all ten kilns were to be fired at the same time as Paul had discovered the problem and was trying to avoid the formation of an explosive mixture of gases. Again, he gave his orders but, as he was about to leave, he was challenged by the redoubtable Donald who, having no chemical knowledge or understanding of the cause of the explosion, was deeply concerned for his men and himself and moved to the point of threatening strike action:

> When the foreman [Donald] demured to proceed till the Dr would explain the Cause of the explosion which wrecked the works so as to be better able to avoid a repetition. To this reasonable request the Dr reluctantly agreed. Demured, actually refused to kindle the Kiln

Furnaces, question to be first answered and explained, knowing that the Gases Generated when the Kilns was Kindled ONE BY ONE Wrecked the Works by Explosion. Is it an unexplosive gas that will be generated by the Kilns being simultaneously kindled [?]. If so What Makes it so [?]. Explain to be understood or stand By Yourself and Kindle the Furnaces.

You can almost see Paul gulping as he felt the power of Morison's simple but forceful intellect, knowing that Donald was right: 'Dr Paul soon after the Explosion sent a Book to the Works, all are Explosive Gases.'

Nobody at the works knew that the gases were explosive and Paul, who understood very well their explosive nature, was relying on trial and error and was seemingly unconcerned about safety. The water joints which he had omitted from his design would have specifically prevented any such explosions. After this stand-off the works began to settle down and operated almost uninterrupted through the winter of 1860 into February 1861, however the results were far from encouraging. Only about 3% of the peat was being converted into tar, slightly better than Kane's figure for the Irish peat but well below the 10% yield which Paul's experiments had led him to expect for the Lewis peat. The disappointment was further deepened by the fact that only half of the planned 100 tons per week of peat was being distilled. Added to these woes of poor performance was the overriding problem of the terrible stench from the fumes which was carried across Stornoway by the prevailing winds. Paul must have felt uncomfortable, if he ventured into Stornoway society, as being the man responsible. In his own objective assessment: 'the smell produced by the escape of this tarry gas into the air was exceedingly offensive for miles around.' Or as Morison put it more subjectively: 'Town and Country Complaining of the sickening and offensive smell from the Works.'

Paul seemed to be out of his depth. He had no grounding in the work of a chemical engineer – who takes reactions that occur in test tubes and makes them happen on a vast scale. The clever chemist/manager and his all-seeing foreman were both in the same boat with regard to understanding what was actually happening at the works: 'Dr Paul and his Foreman was similar, learning through failures and disappointments.'

Although Paul had a certain respect for Donald Morison, he was somewhat disingenuous to the workmen. He later blamed the initial failure of the works as 'owing to the wet-state of the brickworks and to a temporary difficulty with the work people.'

Having been initially impressed by the keen native intelligence of the crofters, later – as the failures at the works grew – Paul changed his regard for them to irritation, seeing them as dull and lazy: 'the inhabitants [of Lewis] accustomed to a rude mode of life, disliking work and strenuously opposed to anything differing from their customary habits, are not easily trained to systematic labour.'

The late Robin MacKenzie of Stornoway, a keen historian of the Lewis Chemical Works, once described Paul as 'a snob and an idealist', qualities which probably allowed Paul to come to this jaundiced view. The frustration created by his enterprise, which wouldn't get off the ground, caused Paul – like Donald Munro – to make scapegoats of the willing crofters.

In the early spring of 1861 things were not going well. Caunter was in Edinburgh seeing his daughters and Paul was convinced that the apparatus he had set up was unworkable. In despair he went south, to London and sought advice, which, when offered, was very simple: 'reconstruct the whole affair.'

Chapter Six

And So to Market

'.... in one word; an enormous, reckless blunder.'
– Donald Morison

Paul returned from the south invigorated and with new ideas for improving the works. As to their perceived failure, he had managed to identify two major problems and their causes, which allowed him to proceed with remedial action. He saw the 'feeble draught' produced by the chimney as the main reason for the poor control that the operators had over the process. The cast iron chimney produced an erratic air supply to the burning peat at the base of the kilns which prevented steady burning. As Paul observed:

> During calm weather the quantity of peat worked was not much more than half that worked when there was a fresh breeze. With a dead calm the action of the kilns would sometimes be entirely stopped and during gales which were of a very frequent occurrence it was impossible to continue working. The

most troublesome effect of these two extremes was the production of back-draught from the chimney through the condensers, towards the kilns by means of which air became mixed with the vapours of combustible gases, and, when this admixture reached a certain limit, explosions sometimes took place which were both inconvenient and dangerous.

Paul had at last become rational about explosions rather than being merely 'put about'! To improve the draught, Paul first considered the highly dubious step of lighting a fire at the base of the chimney; the rising hot air from the fire would help to draw the current of gases through the kilns and condensers. He soon disregarded this as unworkable on account of the inflammable nature of the gases and the 'boisterous' weather conditions, especially in winter.

His practical remedy was to add fire-doors and ash pits to the base of each kiln, covered by a shed. These would be used to regulate the entry of the air and so to allow better burning of the peat. At the top of each kiln he added a mechanism which allowed fresh peat to be added to the kiln without the loss of the foul-smelling gases which had injured the kiln operators. Condensers were made air-tight so that explosive gas mixtures could not form, thus preventing any repetition of the disastrous explosion. The main agent of control was the installation of a fan, driven by an eight inch steam engine. The purpose of the fan was to allow a controlled flow of air to be drawn through the kilns and condensers, regardless of the state of the weather.

Paul chose to draw air through the kilns rather than blow air as Rogers had practiced in Ireland. Drawing air may have provided an easier practical solution given the large number of kilns (ten in total) that would have needed to be connected to any blast system. It may simply have been a desire on Paul's part not to infringe Rogers' patent for the blast kiln, something Paul was quite aware of. In later years Paul was to set up a chemical consultancy in London where he dealt with, among other things, patent litigation.

Paul's reference to 'boisterous weather' is interesting. Weather conditions on Lewis during the 1860s and 1870s were not good; poor weather had prevailed in Scotland from the 1750s and was to continue until the end of the nineteenth century. Weather readings were made by lighthouse keepers and in 1867, the establishment of the Scottish Royal Meteorological Society allowed a more formal record of the weather. During 1871, wind speeds were recorded at Lews Castle – probably by Henry Caunter – with results indicating hurricane strength winds, Force Twelve, on nine days and storm strength, Force Ten, on twenty-four days.

The second failure of the works that Paul recognised was that of the poor yield of only 3%, due in part to the poor draughting, as he explained: 'much tar was condensed among the cold peat at the top of the kiln and this tar melting afterwards, ran down to the fire and was more or less burned and destroyed.'

Efficiency was improved by removing some of the distilled peat charcoal through the fire-doors before it had a chance to burn; more of this was produced than was required to distil subsequent charges of fresh peat. There is no record of what happened to this peat charcoal initially although years later it was marketed.

On turning his attention to the condensers, Paul found plenty of scope for improvement. The condensers worked by simply passing the hot gases through a series of air-cooled, cast-iron pipes where the cooled gases formed a liquid. Paul had tried to introduce a mechanical means of separating the tarry particles out of the gas to help the condensing process. To achieve this, a zig-zag shaped brick-built chamber connecting the condensers to the chimney was filled with bunches of heather taken directly from the moor: a low-tech approach that worked very well. It was subsequently found that the gas escaping from the chimney was tar-free. Unfortunately, this created a new problem, as the chamber soon became blocked with tar which was 'deposited on the branches of heather like drifts of snow.'

To complete his efficiency drive Paul added a belt-and-braces job of scrubber towers at the end of the row of condensers. As the gases were drawn through these tall cylinders, they met a shower of water – pumped in by the steam engine – which Paul hoped would remove the last of the tar from the gas.

Paul's final improvements involved health and safety. The world of predictive health and safety at work was at that time very much in the future. In the nineteenth century it was very much the case that if something looked or proved to be dangerous, operators had to cope with it and hope that eventually the problem would be addressed. Paul added important safety valves and water joints between the kilns and the condensers which isolated the inflammable gases from the flames in the kiln while still allowing free passage of the gases to the condensers. At the other end of the condensers, the water spray in the scrubber towers acted as a safety valve.

The welfare of the men out on the moor was also considered, as a winding drum and hauling gear were added to the drive of the steam engine so that the peat hutches could be pulled up the incline to the works, relieving the men of much toil.

These hopeful improvements took time and money, both of which were in good supply as a result of Henry Caunter enthusiastically extolling the progress Paul was making into James Matheson's ear.

In August 1861, the steam engine wheezed into life and the Schieler's patent fan, produced by the North York Foundry Company, began rotating at 1600 revolutions per minute, sucking air through the kilns and condensers. With the steady chuff-chuff of the exhaust, the whirring of the spinning fan, the heat and flame from the kilns and the steam and smoke from the boiler filling the atmosphere, the industrial revolution had certainly arrived in Lewis to tickle the senses of all.

The whole set-up worked very well; the kiln operators were now in control of their charge rather than the wind dictating the outcome of the process. But any jubilation that Paul and Caunter may have felt was short-lived. After just six hours, the steam engine ground to a halt as the fan jammed in its casing. The tar seemed to go everywhere it should not have, as Morison reported: 'the Engene failed to Work the Fan which was found to be full of Tar in the consistency of Butter, preventing the Fan from revolving.' Paul described the situation in a loftier tone: 'The mechanical action of the fan was found to be very efficacious in separating the suspended tar which appeared to be churned out of the gas by the fan.' The problem was soon resolved by the ever-busy works fitter who rigged up a steam jet to play on the fan, causing the tar to melt and run into a collecting vessel placed below the fan.

The tar was now being collected at the condensers, the scrubber towers, the fan and the heather chamber, which had been retained. Surprisingly, more than half of the tar was collected at the fan. Paul's idea of the mechanical separation of the tar as being effective seems to have been correct. The expensive machinery placed on top of the kilns to make recharging safer – and which cost £80 according to Morison – was found to be redundant, now that the draught could be controlled, and was removed to the growing scrap heap.

The effect of all these alterations was quite staggering. The yield of tar immediately increased from 3% to 5%, as the operators became familiar with the new apparatus, and the number of men required to maintain the kilns fell. The cost of making the tar was reduced from £5 to £3 per ton and the production of the tar rose from six tons to seven tons per week. By the winter of 1861, the works were producing tar in a continuous process, distilling upwards of twenty tons of peat in each twenty-four hour period. Things were going well.

In order to achieve Paul's goal of producing paraffin and entering the lucrative illuminating oil market, the tar had to be treated in a refinery, where it was subjected to various processes using a number of chemicals. It was this part of the process that Henry Caunter had been unable to achieve, leading James Matheson to bring Paul on board. Refining, unlike the initial distillation to produce tar, was not a simple, straightforward step but required know-how. As far as apparatus was concerned a steam engine was essential for refining: it drove the pumps necessary to provide the hydraulic pressure required for filtering and the stirring apparatus for mixing in chemicals at various stages as well as providing essential hot water and steam. Concentrated sulphuric acid, potassium hydroxide, sodium hydroxide, lime and chlorochromic acid were some of the chemicals used to work up the crude tar to produce the various oils and wax. These were all pretty nasty substances to handle and could cause damage to the novice or the unwary. The products themselves – paraffin and light oils – were dangerous if basic safety precautions regarding fire were not adhered to. All in all, unlike the extraction of tar from peat, refining was not an easy process for the uninitiated to quickly become familiar with. Paul's specialist knowledge and guidance were essential. Sir Robert Kane, in his report to Parliament in 1851, had cautioned on the need for a necessarily-remote peat distillation works to have a refinery on site and of the problems that this would create, both economically and for an inexperienced labour force. In other branches of the paraffin industry refiners were experienced, specialist manufacturers.

The refining was initially carried out at the Creed works while a new refinery – part of Paul's grand plan – was being developed. This was built at Garrabost, on the Eye peninsula east of Stornoway and some six miles from the Creed works, where there were large covered sheds at the brickworks available for use. Work on the refinery had started back in 1859 when Paul first arrived and was greeted with much enthusiasm in the press, as the Inverness Courier had reported on 3rd March 1859:

> We believe Sir James Matheson is about to erect extensive chemical works for the manufacture of paraffine etc, from peat moss – the cost of which will be several thousand pounds – at Garrabost near the town of Stornoway. Experiments have already been made by two gentlemen of high reputation [Paul and Caunter] and we understand with a satisfactory result. These works will be the source of employment to a large number of labouring classes.

The brickworks also featured a steam engine and boiler, essential for the refinery, but in a bit of a state after fifteen years of brick making, as Morison described, ever mindful of economies and wasted money: 'The dilapidated state of the Brick sheds and Machinery (the Engene renewed, Steam

Boiler replaced by a New Boiler) and providing as supply of water for condensing purposes etc, incurred Great expence.'

Paul developed the site of the Garrabost brick works into quite an industrial concern which housed not only the complex apparatus for refining the tar, but also accommodation for the skilled workforce required to operate the works. Morison's description is detailed:

> Dr Paul fixed on extensive sheds at the Brick works for the refining apparatus, Stills, Pans, Tanks, Hydrolic Press, and all machinery required for the distillation and refining of the Tar distilled from the Peat at Lewis Chemical Works. He had cottages built for his residents, Houses fitted up for the various tradesman and their families required at the Works – Smithies, Cooperage, Joiners Shop and stables, all supplied with the necessary Matereal and latest improved tools, all fitted up and adjoining the works.

There was also a large chemical store for acids, soda and other chemicals for isolating, deodorising and bleaching the paraffin.

Some local tradesmen were employed: 'Two Blacksmiths, Two Carpenters, One Cooper'. Others were drafted in: a clerk, a riveter and engine fitter; a brick maker and an assistant chemist, William Whithead, who lived with his wife and infant son at Garrabost. Whithead was an analytical chemist who worked in the chemical laboratory that formed part of the industrial complex. Morison stated: 'Dr Paul had fitted up at the Refinery A Laboratory fitted up with small copper stills, Pans and Innumerable Number of Glass Stills Test tubes also a very complicated Ballance under Glass

Cover [weighing machine]. Shelfs full of Bottles which Various Chemicals, In short everything required to conduct Analyses and Experiments.'

The first stage of the refining process involved stirring the crude tar with sulphuric acid which reacted to separate the impurities, mainly pitch. Hot water was then added, on which floated the purified tar which was drawn off and distilled. As the process developed, Paul realised that the water supply at the brickworks was inadequate for all that was going on. The problem was solved by carrying out the first distillation about half a mile to the south of the brickworks, next to a stream, Allt nan Gall, near the head of Glen Dibidale. This was just to the north of the site of the present-day Garrabost Meal Mill (built in 1893).

Stills were built along with a cottage for the workers who were to look after the apparatus. The oral tradition of Garrabost tells that the present road to the village of Bayble from the main Point road (A866) follows the path of the 'Paraffin Road', a track built to bring the peat from the moorland to fire the stills in Glen Dibidale.

A tramway was laid across the moor to connect the brickworks to the stills, which had an average fall towards the stills of about one in thirty. Tar from the Creed works was discharged from horse drawn carts at the brickworks refinery and transferred to small trucks which were manhandled down the slope to the stills in the glen. After the chemistry had been performed on the crude tar, the distilled, purified tar and oils were manhandled back up the tramway to the brickworks refinery for finishing.

The line of the tramway is clearly visible today as it crosses the open moor, arcing out from the brickworks in a gentle curve before straightening towards the Glen. Banks were created as peat was thrown up to give a gradual fall to the gradient although, at the southern end, as the tramway approaches the glen, the gradient increases. Here the track divides and one branch passes horizontally along the sides of the Glen behind the site of the stills. The crude tar could have easily been off-loaded into the stills with the help of gravity. The scar left by this track-bed, hewn into the hillside, is clearly visible. The other branch carried on down the glen to the ground level of the stills where the purified tar and oil could more easily be loaded back onto the trucks for transport back up to the refinery for processing into saleable products.

A few years ago a drainage ditch, which had naturally developed along the line of the tramway as it descended into the glen, was cleared to improve the grazing. Amazingly, it was found that many of the wooden sleepers on which the rails lay were, and still are, in-situ, despite having been covered with many years of peat detritus. It is surprising that the wood is still in place as although the peat would naturally preserve it, timber is always at a premium on an island with virtually no trees.

The sleepers are bolts of sawn timber, nearly regular, about four feet long and four inches square. The rails were of a different type to the bridge rails used at the Creed works. The trucks ran on flat, flangeless wheels and the rails were L shaped, with the raised part sitting on the inside of the wheel. These rails were very strong and hardy. One rail, discovered half in and half out of the peat, although quite corroded where it had been exposed, showed little corrosion where it had been buried in the oxygen-depleted peat. The rails were simply laid across the sleepers at intervals of ten feet or so and held in place by thick iron nails in groups of four. The exact mechanism for attachment is not known.

The foundations of the tramway consisted of a mixture of stones, broken bricks and broken tiles. Horseshoes found amongst this debris would indicate that ponies were probably used to help pull the trucks on the uphill journey to the refinery. The oral tradition of Garrabost also tells of the hoisting of sails on the trucks just as Donald Morison's daughter had witnessed at the Creed works. Down in the glen there is plenty of evidence of past activity by man. Some years ago, before the drainage ditch was opened up, the remains of a brick wall could be seen in the bank of the ditch. The surface of the ground looks disturbed and reed beds have formed.

Graham Morrison, who grew up and has lived most of his life at the Garrabost Mill – where his late father, John Morrison, was the Garrabost miller – made the discoveries of the iron rails and the wooden sleepers whilst recently burying a dead sheep. He also came across a brick wall, probably a foundation for the stills. In one particular area, Graham relates how the ground takes on an oily sheen when the weather is particularly wet indicating an underlying source of hydrocarbon, perhaps accumulated tar spillage from filling and emptying the stills.

Graham also has two curious cast-iron pots. These flanged domes are about eighteen inches in diameter and are made of thick iron. One of the castings has an inlet manifold with a half inch hole. Graham remembers his father stopping the hole with a bolt and using the domes as cattle feeding pots. They may have been part of the stills or condensers; the tops of the scrubber towers with a water spray inlet or the cap of a condenser or still. The area would benefit from a professional archaeological investigation.

The Lewis Chemical Works continued to grow, from one site to three. These individual sites had specific functions: at the Creed Works crude tar was produced from peat: the Knock Works were where the crude tar was purified; and at the Garrabost Works paraffin was produced at the refinery. However adding the Knock Works doubled the transport costs from the Creed as well as increasing capital costs. How did Paul allow this apparently haphazard, inefficient state of affairs to develop when he had all the space on the island to work with? As he was responsible for the brickworks as well as the chemical works, it would have suited him to live at Garrabost where he could oversee the production. In his usual forthright and passionate assessment of the situation – but with a hint of irony – Donald Morison was later to pen some memorable lines on this separation:

> The Questions May arise. Why was the Lewis Chemical Works thus separated into Three departments and not save Sir James Matheson, Bt, the Enormous Expense incurred by such separation When there was such a field to select a Site where all could be together having plenty of water, Peat and also clear from a Fishing River. My answer to this question is in one word, *AN ENORMOUS RECKLESS BLUNDER*, which the Responsible Parties, Messrs Paul and Caunter called by a More refined Term *AN ERROR OF JUDGEMENT*.

When Morison originally wrote these words, such was his temper that, on re-reading, he inserted the word 'reckless' into 'an enormous blunder' to make his condemnation of the situation absolutely clear.

The complete process from peat to paraffin might not have been at its most efficient, but the years of planning, building and testing were showing results. Paul's plans and hopes came to fruition when, on the 19th October 1861, an advert appeared in the Glasgow Herald, announcing to the world the sale of 'Lignole – a new and superior illuminating oil available from J&T Wilson, 117 Argyll Street, Glasgow at 3s 6d [17½p] per gallon.' Thus Lignole joined the newspaper advertisement columns, alongside lighting oil adverts for Saxoline Oil, Young's Pale and Common Paraffine, and Belmontine Oil. The merchant Matheson had arrived in the illuminating oil market, and the light shone on his hopes and aspirations for the employment of his tenants on Lewis.

These adverts featured weekly throughout October, November and December of 1861, not ceasing until the 26th February 1862 when all the illuminating oil manufacturers stopped subscribing as the evenings lengthened and the lamps were left unlit. How Lignole was received by the buying public remains a mystery. At the time Paul had a sample independently examined by Dr Anderson of Glasgow University who commented that 'it would compare favourably with the best varieties of mineral oil obtained from coal.' It appeared that Matheson had at last set in motion the revolution which, in his own words, would 'increase the resources of the island and better the condition of the inhabitants.'

Chapter Seven

Paul goes South Again

'Frankly told the reasons for such a sudden change.
Not necessary here to repeat.'
– Donald Morison

The production of Lignole continued throughout the winter of 1861/62. Paul was trying to break into the growing illuminating oil market to compete with the established products: Belmontine Oil, Young's Paraffine Oil, Saxoline Oil and St Mungo Paraffine Oil. These were produced from coal, shale and tar deposits, and their superlative descriptions vied with each other for the market share.

With the advent of coal gas, paraffin wax and paraffin oil, there was now quite a choice of lighting sources for both town and country dwellers. These were all an improvement on the traditional spermaceti candles made from a waxy substance found in the heads of whales which, when burned, produced a poor light and a bad smell. Oil made from whale blubber was becoming scarce as the whale was becoming harder to find, having been hunted almost to extinction. Paraffin oil and paraffin wax candles were portable and gave out an excellent light without the well-known explosive dangers associated with coal gas, which was only available to those living within the distance of a gas main running from a gas works.

James Young produced the first paraffin oil on an industrial scale in 1851, at his Bathgate Works which was reckoned to have been the world's first refinery. Here, the local shale – known as Torbanehill mineral – gave a large yield of good quality paraffin. By the time that Lignole came to the market some ten years later, the Bathgate Works were well developed, covering some twenty acres and employing over seven hundred men.

There were no recorded accidents in the history of the Bathgate Works. Unlike other branches of the chemical industry paraffin had a good safety record. Paraffin oil was inherently safe as it would only burn on a wick in a lamp and the liquid was virtually fireproof at room temperature. Put a match into a bowl of paraffin and it will go out but if the oil is heated, it will gradually become flammable. There is a certain temperature – the flash point – above which the liquid itself will continually burn. For Young's oil this temperature was about 140°F (60°C), making it very safe to use in lamps and easy to store and handle. It could be poured quite safely in the naked light of a candle and an upset lamp would not necessarily start a fire.

Unfortunately, cheap oil imported from the USA and Canada – known as Rock oil – was also being sold under the name of paraffin. This oil contained large amounts of naphtha and petrol which made it very inflammable and consequently dangerous to use and handle. This led to many accidents and some fatalities as unscrupulous traders adulterated paraffin with petrol to make it go further or because paraffin producers were careless when refining the crude oil. In August 1861, the Glasgow Herald was exhorting consumers to apply a simple test to their paraffin: 'Fill a teacup half full of the oil, take it out of doors and dip into it a lighted match. If the oil burns on withdrawal of the lighted match, it is dangerous to use and not Patent Paraffin Oil.' That August one could probably tell the Glasgow Herald readers by their singed eyebrows!

Despite the commercial challenges of the established market, Paul had his eye on the ball. He saw the significance of the burning properties of Lignole. Like Young's Patent Paraffin, Lignole also needed to be heated to a high temperature before it would burn. At 200°F (93°C), its flash point was higher than Young's oil and this, together with its excellent illuminating power, made Lignole a winner. In January 1862, the adverts for Lignole changed to reflect and capitalise on its positive nature: 'Lignole – A superior Oil, for burning in Belmontine and Paraffin lamps without any risk of explosion.'

As the year progressed, the problem of dangerous paraffin was being investigated. Scientific papers were published and commissions acted. In July 1862, the government passed the Act for the Safe Keeping of Petroleum, which set limits on the storage of paraffin and defined the substance as having a minimum flashpoint of 100°F (38°C).

Meanwhile, back on Lewis, the successful winter of 1861/62 still had a few shocks in store for the Lewis Chemical Works. One night in December 1861, as the engineman was inspecting the works, lighting his way with a naked flame, escaping gas at the fan caught fire: 'a naked light accidentaly Catched on the Gas which Burnt in a Tremendous Flame as it mixed with the Air, Lighting the surrounding Hills.' The workers, fearing another explosion, abandoned the place. It was left to Donald Morison to save the day by slowing the engine and flooding the water joints, thus preventing anything other than minor damage.

Paul arrived the next morning, was very interested to hear that the gas burned and requested a detailed report. After a few days the works were back in production but with an added improvement – a gas burner – which no doubt delighted the delicate noses of the Stornoway burghers. At last an answer had presented itself as to the problem of smell. It is strange that the idea of burning the gas had not occurred to Paul earlier; the use of peat gas as a fuel was well known and Paul had even written about the subject. In 1858, he had reviewed the work of Dr Vohl on peat distillation in Germany: 'The gas given off maybe advantageously used for heating'.

Morison's description of the lighting of the gas burner seems to indicate that Henry Caunter had become further out of his depth regarding the workings of the Lewis Chemical Works, even to the extent of becoming a bit of a laughing stock to Paul:

> Our worthy Paymaster, Mr Caunter, accompanied Dr Paul to the Works. But, not aware that the gas was to be Kindled, was greatly alarmed for his Bodly saftey, Earnestly desired the Match witheld till he got to a safe distance, Predicted an explosion of the Whole Affair, Managed up to the Lochs Road, before he looked back to see as he expected the whole show blown to the Air, Dr Paul greatley amused by Mr Caunter's alarm for his personal safety.

Henry Caunter didn't enjoy the personal relationship that Donald Morison and Benjamin Paul had developed, based on mutual respect for each other's strengths and abilities. Henry must have felt that he was out of the loop as far as the development of the works was concerned: 'the relation between Dr Paul and Mr Caunter was not of such a Friendly Nature as to lead to Chemical Knowledge being imparted.'

Henry survived and the works carried on day and night until the end of March 1862, when a problem arose over water supply – the folly of building on high ground was becoming apparent. This break in operations allowed the tramways to be extended and the doubling of the number of hutches to twenty. The operations were such that the nightshift would empty these twenty hutches which were left full each evening. More brickwork was also completed as foundations were laid for stills and evaporating pans.

Paul's original business plan was to produce only paraffin from the peat, but he now decided to produce sulphate of ammonia, an excellent fertiliser, for the development of Matheson's new Lews Castle grounds and gardens. The manufacture involved mixing the diluted, purified waste acid from the refining process at Garrabost with the watery liquid which separated from the tar in the condensers at the Creed works. This liquid was also a waste product, regularly discharged into the Creed River when no salmon were running. Fuelled by the recently discovered combustible peat gas, this fertiliser production helped to eliminate dangerous waste products and to produce something really useful.

By April, everything was going smoothly again. The main product – Lignole – had hit the market and the by-product – sulphate of ammonia – was about to appear on the local market. Paul had spent over three years developing, adapting and improving his plans, working towards Matheson's aim of developing the natural resources of Lewis and using the new science to improve the lot of the islands' inhabitants. Paul was very hopeful for the future as Morison related: 'Everything now looked promising for the success of the Lewis Chemical Works which as Dr Paul said, was now at a stage when he could profitably apply his Chemical

Knowledge, and forget his many disappointments in Lewis for the Last 3 years.'

Donald Morison's common sense approach to life and people probably led Paul to confide in him. This friendship led to a sensational revelation: 'On his visiting the Works First Week of April he (Dr Paul) looked unusually out of Sorts. Remarked it likely that he was soon to leave the Works (Frankly told the reasons for such a change. Not necessary here to repeat).' For Morison this news must have come like a bolt from the blue. Morison had major, delegated responsibilities; to his workforce, to Matheson, and to his family- all of which he took very seriously. Paul left for London indicating that he would know for certain in ten days if he was to return. On 22nd April, Paul let it be known that he would not be returning to the island. For the Lewis Chemical Works it was the end of an era.

Why did Paul leave, apparently so suddenly? Morison indicates that there was more than one reason for Paul's departure. Morison's account was written about thirty-five years after the event and the fact that he chose not to elaborate on the reasons could indicate that he did not wish to cause any upset to anyone or to sully a memory. So it is left to speculation. Did Paul have other offers of employment or more urgent ambitions to fulfil? Did he want to get away from a continually frustrating situation, compounded by the workforce, weather and midges? It is possible that his contract had simply terminated and he needed to find a new source of finance, or that he was missing the scientific and literary stimulation that London provided. Or perhaps there were personal reasons, such as escaping from a romantic entanglement?

Paul's assistant, William Whithead, left Garrabost at the same time as Paul, which points to a professional rather than personal reason for departure. (Whithead had no desire to step into Paul's shoes but, since he was never acknowledged in Paul's papers or makes any further appearance in the literature of chemistry, he probably remained a technical assistant.) However the late Duncan MacLeod of Garrabost recalled his grandfather telling of a doctor at the brickworks who ran off with a local girl! In all likelihood the truth will never be known and as the late Lewis historian James Shaw Grant once reflected: 'Relationships are always more complex than the oral tradition remembers.'

Working with Henry Caunter would have severely tried Paul; the loquacious amateur would scarcely have endeared himself to the objective, sarcastic, die-hard scientist who didn't suffer fools. Paul also had to suffer the folly of one of his workmen. Just before his departure, Paul had given notice to a Garrabost brick maker, James MacFadyen, for intemperance, amongst other reasons. Paul mentioned 'a temporary difficulty with the work people' in 1860 which perhaps points to his relationship with MacFadyen.

In his writings Paul paints an unflattering picture of the Lewisman as disliking work and being opposed to new experiences. The sarcastic and abrasive Paul probably misconstrued the canny and cautious welcome of the Lewisman for ignorance and foolishness, especially when spoken to in Gaelic rather than English. Paul could probably only deal with the intellect when it came to the workers. He would have done well to follow his friend and fellow industrial chemist, Edward Charles Stanford, who set up a Chemical Works in Tiree in 1862 for the efficient burning of seaweed to extract iodine. Stanford gave evidence to the Napier Commission in 1884 on the project and its effects on the lives of the crofters. His assessment of their acceptance of him is insightful:

The difficulty of getting people to work was considerable. Very little English was spoken and of course an interpreter was always by my side. Then the most extraordinary rumours were set about; some thought the Sassenach was a Frenchman, and their ideas about Napoleon were still very warlike; indeed every nationality claimed me in turn. Others thought my object was to dig up the dead bodies and boil them down for the fat (there was little of that to spare then amongst the living); others, the majority, took a violent hatred against me, because they thought I was an excise officer sent to look after the illicit stills. They would do nothing for me; they would sell me nothing. Bread and meat could not be got and much fine turbot and halibut was cut up for bait, but not for me. However, this did not last long, and I soon got on very well with them; for I had promised to employ the people as much as possible. The promise has been kept and after a long experience I can speak highly of their faithful service when their confidence is gained.

Lewis social life must have seemed spartan to Paul compared to London life with the buzz of his bohemian chums to provide relaxing enlightenment as well as the developing scientific scene of regular lectures at various societies. Paul was well aware of developments occurring in many branches of the chemical industry, especially in the rapidly changing area of new energy sources and technology. He held a conviction that the development of coal gas manufacture was very advantageous and he was the main witness giving evidence to the Royal Commission on Coal Supply which reported in 1866.

In 1863, Young's patent on paraffin production expired, a patent that he had vigorously defended as others had tried to capitalise on his process or to apply the patent to other minerals. Other operators moved into the Lothians' shale oil fields and production of paraffin rose. Young's works alone were producing 116,000 gallons of paraffin a week; the Lewis Chemical Works was producing less than two percent of this volume.

In 1859 – six months after Paul had started work in Lewis – Edwin Drake struck oil in the world's first oil well which had been drilled at Titusville, Pennsylvania, USA, and from which paraffin was isolated. The price of the crude oil fell from $29 a barrel in 1859 to $1 a barrel in 1861 and by September 1862 imports of Canadian oil were exceeding demand. In the spring of 1862 the writing was on the wall; within a few years there was crisis in the paraffin industry. Paul would see all these developments rapidly overtaking his dogged efforts with the soggy Lewis peat. Concerns about the cost of raw peat was always on Paul's mind as the works grew. Charles Stanford commented on peat supply to his own works: 'There is this peculiarity about peat; that if a manufactory requires a large supply, the cost will necessarily increase with the quantity required, because a larger area must be worked. The peat distillery in Lewis, started under Sir J Matheson by my friend Dr Paul, although very well laid out, was no exception to this universal rule.'

Paul was very ambitious and his subsequent career reveals that he did not want to be stuck in a commercial cul-de-sac with little prospect of challenge and enlightenment. In one of his obituary notices there is reference to his attitude to business when compared to science: 'for one of his perfervid intensity of conviction, it must have been increasingly difficult to subdue his mind and hand to a medium in which science had to compromise with business.' Paul had plenty reasons to bail out.

In a letter to Lewis historian Frank Thompson written in the 1960s, Donald Morison's grandson Donald Robertson Morison stated that Paul was 'eased out' of the Lewis Chemical Works, but by whom he did not relate. In 1981 he referred to Paul's leaving in more robust terms: 'His [Paul's] removal from control of the Works was a scandalous piece of jobbery.' The fact that Paul returned to the island as a visitor just a few years after he left however, suggests that Paul and Matheson parted on good terms. Young Morison's sentiment simply adds to the mystery.

As far as James Matheson was concerned, Paul's departure was a great loss. Not all were dismayed at Paul's leaving however; significantly, Morison emphasises the feelings of those at the Garrabost refinery: 'but [Paul] did not [return], to the great loss of Sir James Matheson, Bt, and all concerned in the work EXCEPTING those EMPLOYED at the REFINERY.'

In the autumn of 1862 the oil lamps of Glasgow were trimmed once more as the days shortened but Lignole was notably absent from the adverts for illuminating oil in the Glasgow Herald. It would be a few years before the name would appear once again in print. In that spring of 1862, strange happenings were about to take place amongst the kilns and condensers of the Lewis Chemical Works and Henry Caunter was to have some testing times of his own.

With the ascendancy of a group of Irish workers at the Garrabost refinery and brickworks, led by the intemperate James MacFayden and known by Morison as 'the clique', a new phase of the Lewis Chemical Works was beginning, in which business management practice, commercial ventures and scientific methods of research were to take on a new light. Ironically this was to temporarily extinguish those lamps so carefully lit by Dr Benjamin Horatio Paul.

Chapter Eight

Under New Management

'Why get a chemist when I can do it.'
– James MacFadyen

On the 22nd of April 1862, Donald Munro, Matheson's factor, accompanied Henry Caunter to the Creed works, adding gravitas to the occasion of the introduction of Henry to the workforce as the 'future Manager of the Lewis Chemical Works in place of Dr Paul.'

Caunter was no doubt pleased with his new appointment. Compared to the original works which he and Wilson had set up in 1857, he was now in charge of a works that was extracting tar on a grand scale with relative reliability, and the mysterious process of extracting paraffin from the tar had been successfully developed into a production line for a lighting oil which was now in the market.

With Donald Morison as the tar production foreman, Henry had no fear that he would need to have much input into the day-to-day running of the Creed works. On the other hand, the operation of the refinery required an in-depth knowledge which was beyond Caunter's ken – that was what had led to Paul's appointment as chemist three years previously. So on the evening of the same day, Henry got straight to work in Glen House. He wrote out an advert for a chemist to take responsibility for the Garrabost refinery and brickworks, to be placed in the Glasgow Herald. He also wrote a letter to Sir James Matheson – at that time in London – requesting to be provided with a pony and trap to enable him to carry out his management duties between the Stornoway and Garrabost sites. That same night Caunter had a meeting with his foreman, Donald Morison, whom he used as a sounding board for his plans. Present at that meeting was the Garrabost brickmaker James MacFadyen.

James MacFadyen had come to Garrabost as a brickmaker along with his wife Janet and three children, probably around 1860, from Kilmaurs in Ayrshire, where he had worked as a brick and tile maker. He probably worked at the large Moorfield Tile Works where his brother Hugh had previously worked. A number of MacFadyen's family and associates were to join him at Garrabost over the next few years; notably, his brother Hugh who arrived in 1865. Morison repeatedly – and disapprovingly – refers to the 'Irish Clique' that gradually settled to work and live at the brickworks and who left their mark on the village years after they had left. The area of Upper Garrabost where the clay pits are found is still known as Buaile MacPhadhain (MacFadyen's enclosure) and the clay quarry as Garadh MacPhadhain (MacFadyen's lair).

The oral tradition of Garrabost recalls how Irish 'strangers' worked at the brickworks. The village became noted for its Irish community, which was not always to the villagers' liking! The late Sandy MacLeod of Garrabost recalled his schooldays in the 1920s when he fought with boys from Lower Bayble who used to taunt him with '*Eirannaich Garrabost*' (The Irish from Garrabost). The late Duncan MacLeod of Garrabost would tell of the children's rhyme:

> *Coin Bhreag na h-Airde, Ladies Bheag Shiadair,*
> *Merlich Phabail, S'Eirrannaich Gharraboist.*
> (Spotted dogs of Aird, young ladies of Shader,
> Thieves of Bayble, Irish of Garrabost.)

Some of the Irish workers were thought to have lived in turf huts next to Allt nan Gall (River of Strangers), the river that flowed down the glen where the stills were sited. The raised turf walls of several huts are still apparent to those who know where to look.

According to census records, James was born about 1830 in Kilmaurs although this seems doubtful. His brother Hugh, about seven years his senior, always recorded his own birthplace as Ireland. The oral tradition of Garrabost refers to potters in white aprons who worked with the clay and that the potters had come from Donegal. Morison referred to James MacFadyen's origins in his own description which is not very encouraging: 'The Irish Brick Maker and Famly looked as if they were long out of Employment. But soon proved that strong Drink had to do with their poor appearance – when the Brick Maker and Famly arrived it would be a difficulty to know what was the origin of their Close [clothes?].'

The New Statistical Account for Ayr of 1845 refers to the great influx of 'strangers, chiefly from Ireland' – escaping from the ravages of the famine – and to the great number of 'licences to retail ardent spirits' whereby 'the temptations to intemperance are indefinitely multiplied'. It probably wasn't just MacFadyen's love of the drink that caused problems; David Crabbe makes an interesting observation on Donald Morison's assessment of James MacFadyen: 'Morison's contempt for the man [MacFadyen] and his cronies needs to be seen, and interpreted, through the anti-Irish sentiment of the day, complete with religious overtones. In his manuscript Morison never misses a chance to comment disfavourably on MacFadyen, and with some justification.'

Despite, or perhaps because of his own weakness, James MacFadyen was a quick-witted man of a persuasive nature who understood the weaknesses of other people's characters and how to exploit them. His actions show him to be a character of low cunning, an accomplished, convincing liar and a subtle manipulator, able to contrive a situation to his own advantage, especially when money was concerned. Some six weeks before Paul left Lewis, he had given MacFadyen two months notice of dismissal from the Garrabost brickworks, in May 1862. Paul had been very disappointed with him for a number of reasons, quite apart from intemperance.

When MacFadyen was summoned to Glen House by his new manager that April evening he was in for a pleasant surprise. As there were plenty of orders for brick at Garrabost – enough to keep him busy until July – Caunter had decided to rescind Paul's notice of dismissal. He also informed MacFadyen that the position of chemist at Garrabost was to be advertised, to find a replacement for Paul to run the refinery and brickworks. The wily MacFadyen saw this appointment as another possible threat to his employment and, as his wits were working flat out, his blarney kicked in to land him the deal of the century. As Morison later recalled:

> James MacFadyen thanked Mr Caunter for delaying his Dismissal, rising as to leave the Room. Proved that he had a mind above 'Clay and Brick', congratulated Mr Caunter

as his advancement as manager, and added with emphasis *WHEN A CHEMIST COMES TO THE WORKS YOU WILL BE ONLY MANAGER IN NAME.* Why get a chemist when I can do it. Wonderful to relate, Instead of laughing at the Irish Brickmaker for his audacity, Mr Caunter replied by saying 'Well James in that case a chemist need not be advertised for the Refinery.'

You can sense Morison's incredulity as he witnessed MacFadyen's outrageous guile.

Since 1859, Henry Caunter had been living and working in the shadow of Benjamin Paul as far as the Lewis Chemical Works was concerned and MacFadyen's words had crystallised Caunter's idea that he could once again become the leading scientific brain behind Matheson's plans for the islands' people. Morison despaired for Caunter's gullibility and lack of responsibility for the proper running of the works and to his employer, James Matheson. Morison's contempt for Caunter's over-inflated sense of worth was tempered by his sense of propriety:

> What absurdness. A Common Brick Maker who scarcely could write his Name to be given the position on which depended the profitable Utilizing of the Products of a Work which Cost so much Money. Risk all and Save My Dignity as Manager. In this case Mr Caunter had sense but no reason, otherwise was an agreeable gentleman ... Mr Caunter instead of being subordinate to Dr Paul was now Jubelant. The respect due to him as Manager safer with MacFadyen and his Associates Than with a qualified Chemist.

The die had been cast. The new management regime that was to follow was a fragmented, empire-building affair. MacFadyen and Caunter were based at the refinery at Garrabost, MacFadyen eventually running the day-to-day operation and Caunter carrying out his version of research and development. According to Alasdair Maciver of Milngavie, who recollected the brickworks from the early part of the twentieth century, MacFadyen had the reputation of being a bit of a slave driver. The brickworks was probably not a happy place.

Donald Morison was based at the Creed works, which he ran with his usual common sense approach. Free to use his initiative, he set about improving his charge:

> The Foreman being in charge at the Creed since the First brick was laid ... Had bit by bit understood the requirements of the Work and the Nature of the Dangerous Gases etc ... could now apply Practical Knowledge to the improving Works without much interference from our New Manager who did not pretend any knowledge of the affair, But was for Courtesy sake consulted occationaly.

Morison saw the weaknesses in the design of the works and responded. A large vat (2,000 gallons) was built to collect the tar and water from the condensers. Tar pits were dug near the cart road, each to store thirty tons of tar whilst it was cooling, before being carted to Garrabost. To increase the efficiency more condensers were added between the fan and the gas burner and the exhaust steam from the boiler was used to heat the tar and ammonia water mixture to bring about separation instead of burning peat to provide the heat.

So on the 20th September 1862, five months after Paul's departure, the Lewis Chemical Works were again fired up.

Morison's improvements at once became apparent. After a week, the efficiency of the tar production rose from 5% – the minimum set by Paul for profitability – to 7% and, within a fortnight, to 8.5%.

Morison was very keen to use the peat gas produced by the peat distillation which was simply being burned. He suggested to Henry Caunter that the gas should be used to keep up steam in the boiler, but Henry, being a responsible manager who had a history of nervousness in dealing with the gas, placed a veto on this modification. Morison, selecting his experience and observations over Caunter's fears, went ahead with the plan anyway, laying underground flues and valves to take the gas to the boiler. This action immediately saved three and a half tons of peat a day, peat which could now be distilled and turned into profit. It took Caunter five days to notice the innovation – he had been busy at Garrabost – and he was apoplectic when he discovered that his orders had been ignored. This almost proved to be the end of Morison's involvement with the Lewis Chemical Works, as he related: 'He [Caunter] entirely lost Temper, quite lost Controll of himself, for as he said, daring to do what he prohibited, and if safe to do Dr Paul would have done it when at the works, Predicting the blowing up of the Works etc. His Mildest Term was stuborn disabedience. Left the Works in a rage.' Morison reacted to Caunter's haranguing with the characteristic calm of a man who knows his worth. He had been offered good employment elsewhere, and Caunter knew it: 'A Few Lines sent after him with a Month's notice to get another to take Charge at Creed, seeing the experience gained by being in Charge … was not Valued by him.' Henry slept on these words and, realising that he relied on Morison and, having already lost Paul, he acted decisively: 'Next Morning he came to the Works all mildness and open to reason with him.'

Caunter offered Morison a year's contract but Morison was in no mood to sign. He was irked further by Caunter's behaviour when the latter had arrived at the works with Sir James Matheson and guests and had proceeded to steal Morison's thunder: '[Caunter] returned with Sir James Matheson and several gentleman, then Visitors at the Castle, and with Hat in hand showed them the Gas keeping up steam, which he *ONLY YESTERDAY COMPLETED*.'

Matheson was also made aware of Morison's situation and in an unusual move for him, became involved in the running of the show. Morison submitted to Mathseon's counsel and signed the contract, as he recalled: 'But in a few Days yielded to the *NOBLE* and *BENEVOLENT SIR JAMES'S* advice, saying I would never have reason to repent staying in his Service. In this way I was engrafted into the Lewis C. Works.' Morison had signed against his own better judgement, as he was to make plain later on.

As time proceeded Morison made other innovations. The ammonia water from the condensers, produced after it had been separated from the tar, was problematic. In its raw state it was quite poisonous, especially to fish, as Caunter had discovered in 1850 in the Castle pond. Paul had been addressing the problem before he left the works, leaving his half-finished plans for Caunter to grapple with. Morison dealt with the problem initially by digging large ponds below the works in which the ammonia water was stored. Under the direction of the estate gamekeeper this water was released into the nearby stream which fed into the Creed when the latter was in flood. Despite this precaution, salmon fry still suffered as a result of underground seepage. Morison next arranged for the ammonia water to be released into the ash pits to cool the hot charcoal. This produced an excellent fertiliser which was used for the planting being undertaken in the Castle Grounds.

Morison also developed a novel system of producing lime, essential for sweetening the acid, peaty soils of Lewis, for producing lime mortar and for white-washing. Spurred on by the observations of one of their guests regarding sea shells, Sir James and Lady Matheson started a scheme of employment for their tenants which involved collecting shells from the southern shore of Broad Bay, close to Stornoway. These shells could be burned to produce lime. Lime was usually made by burning limestone, the main source being the lime works at Larne, in Ireland. Sea shells have the same chemical composition as limestone and therefore could be used as a substitute.

Kilns were built in the Castle Grounds but were not successful. The operation was transferred to the Creed works where a furnace was built, to be fired by the plentiful supply of peat gas. This arrangement proved most successful, not only for supplying lime for the Castle Grounds improvements, but also for the tenants, as Morison related: 'scores of Crofters in the adjoining Villages [to Broad Bay], Paid heavy arrears of rent by gathering and carting the shells to Creed Works.'

This project gives an insight into the way Matheson's estate was run. Matheson saw good ideas and passed them along his management chain – in whom he seemed to have total trust – for implementation. This did not require him to actually become involved. Unfortunately, his trust was misplaced, as Morison explained: 'In this manner all the Lime required for Estate Work could have been Burnt at about half the cost of Irish Lime, The Broad Bay supplying the Shells. All such discouraged by Estate officials. No tips from Lime Agents or Ships owners.'

Port records show that in 1866 all the lime cargos were brought in on local boats but later other ship owners plied their trade. Could this have been Donald Munro, the hated factor, who was also chairman of the recently established Harbour Commission in Matheson's frequent absence, sticking his oar in yet again?

Visitors to the Castle, especially from the world of science, were keen to see the Lewis Chemical Works, which were particularly successful when compared to the highly promoted Irish Peat Works. After Caunter's visit, which had so annoyed Morison, the latter was always diplomatic with visitors, keen to keep the ship on an even keel: 'I made it a rule. When Gentlemen visited The Works By saying, If Mr Caunter was present he would explain the operation Better than I could. Professors Tyndall and Fairfax and Huxley doubted this as did others who visited the works.' Henry's ability as a scientist did not cut the mustard with the cognoscenti.

Morison mentions many of the visitors by name. John Tyndall was a physicist who discovered what is now called the Tyndall effect, which occurs when light shines through certain liquids. Thomas Huxley was a biologist and a champion of Charles Darwin, known as 'Darwin's Bulldog'. Both men were popularisers of science. Huxley visited Stornoway in September 1862, with Dr Lyon Playfair, Professor of Chemistry at Edinburgh University. They were members of the Commission on the Herring Fisheries, collecting evidence for a report to be published the following year. It was Lyon Playfair who had first brought James Young's attention to the Derbyshire oil deposits which eventually led to the production of paraffin in the Lothians in the 1850s. Dr Angus Smith, was an eminent chemist and government analyst. 'A titled Irish Gentleman' who had knowledge of the Irish Peat Works – and who may have been Sir Robert Kane – reflected with irony on the presence of James MacFadyen, without actually naming him: 'If the Irish Chemists who erected the Irish Peat Company Works had known to put up a Work like that [the Lewis Chemical Works], The Peat Bogs would have enriched Ireland. They, he said, Could analyze a *FLY'S LEG* in a Laboratory, But an Irish Poteen Distiller Could teach them to Distill the Bog.'

It was a culture of dishonesty and bullying in which Morison, Caunter and MacFadyen were to find themselves. Morison stood aloof from it, although he undoubtedly knew what was going on. MacFadyen was to embrace it, but hapless Henry Caunter seemed oblivious to it, eventually succumbing to its chaos.

Chapter Nine

The Years of Expansion

'Creed Works, Knock Works –
Pitch, Grease and Crude Oil Distilleries
Garrabost Works –
Grease, Oil and Paraffin etc Refinery'
– 1867 Advert: Post Office Glasgow Directory

After Paul's departure, Caunter and MacFadyen found themselves with a working refinery which was capable of producing lighting oil for a ready market. The only problem was that neither of the two knew how to properly operate the works to make the Lignole, despite MacFadyen's assurances to Caunter. It was probably a question of trial and error, as according to Morison, Caunter and MacFadyen were left: 'Grouping [sic] in the Dark to discover the proper manner of Mixing Chemicals and purifying Oils etc.'

Although Morison does not mention him, they may have been helped in their challenge by Kenneth MacLeod, a native of Stornoway, a labourer who lived with Paul at Garrabost. There would have been plenty of opportunity during his time working with Paul to pick up the rudiments of refining the tar. In the 1871 census, Macleod was noted as an 'oil manufacturer', living in Upper Garrabost at a time when the refinery was still in operation.

The first attempts at refining were very much a failure for Caunter and MacFadyen. When Caunter took over the reins as manager, there were thirty-five tons of tar at the Creed works waiting to be refined. This was carted to Garrabost and 'refined' to fill thirty wooden casks, each with thirty gallons of Lignole. The casks were duly despatched to Glasgow but, when they were opened, the paraffin oil was found to be so thick that it would not flow out of the casks. The whole consignment was promptly returned to Garrabost. The two chemists persevered and, eventually they succeeded in their task and Lignole returned to the market.

As a direct result of their ignorance, any waste material from the refinery, such as pitch and acid, was allowed to run away into Broad Bay, an important fishery. Once again, as at the Castle and then the Creed works, fish were the casualty. The farmer at Gress, Mr Liddel, complained of oil and tar being blown on to the shore at Back, on the far side of Broad Bay. Later, it was discovered that the pitch was useful and could be sold after suitable treatment, which involved purifying by boiling, as Morison explained: 'The Pitch when Boiled was found equal to Paltic [Baltic] Pitch and supereor to Coal Tar for Felt Roofing, and Mixed with Peat Dross [granular peat], When cool, Broke up supereor to Coal for Generating Steam.'

Tar was usually imported to the island from Archangel each autumn, but in 1866 and 1867 there were no such imports – the island had become self-sufficient in tar.

Whilst all this activity was going on at the refinery, Caunter was busy carrying out his investigations into other ways of exploiting the peat tar. It had come to his notice that the crude tar had useful properties as a lubricant; Paul had investigated a lubricating oil derived from the tar. Using his pony and trap as a mobile test-bed, Caunter set about trialing the suitability of the tar as a grease for the markets. The results were very encouraging, so much so that in July 1863 he applied for and received provisional protection for his discovery from the Patent Office (Patent No. 1678). In June of the following year he was granted Letters Patent (No 3290), for the invention of 'Improvements in the Manufacture of Lubricating Matter or Composition'. The invention was reported in the Glasgow Herald in December 1864:

> In the course of the manufacture [of paraffin] the intelligent and accomplished manager of the extensive works erected by Sir James Matheson, Bart, MP, was struck by the apparent lubricating properties of a preparation made by him from the tar distilled from the peat. By way of experiment, he resolved to test its powers on the axles of his own gig, which was driven from 16 to 18 miles daily for above three months, and on examination, at the end of that period, it was found to answer beyond his most sanguine expectations – the axles and bushes being in a capital working order. He immediately took the precaution of protecting it by patent.

Product development and testing was a simple affair! With the wheels of industry turning everywhere, lubricants were in demand, no more so than by expanding railways and on a number of Railway Boards sat Matheson. The Herald continued: 'It is now used on railways and consequently well adapted for all descriptions of vehicles – such as carts, wagons, carriages etc – being equal to any other grease on the market and infinitely cheaper.'

Morison gives a favourable account of Caunter's discovery and the way in which the markets reacted: 'The tar after the Pitch was removed or separated was found very suitable as a Lubricator for Waggon Axiles and heavy Machinery. A demand at a profitable price sprang up, orders increasing 'till the Demand was equal to the supply.'

Henry was on to a winner. The Glasgow Herald article was picked up by other banners the length and breadth of the country, from the Northern Ensign to the Western Times, bringing the news to Henry's native Ashburton. In the Inverness Advertiser however, the editor pointedly deleted the phrase 'intelligent and accomplished' in reference to Caunter.

The process for making the grease, outlined in the patent, was simple and elegant, allowing different grades of grease to be made for different uses. The tar was mixed with caustic soda solution and stirred; this caused it to break up and produce the raw lubricant material. To this Caunter added 5 – 10% of palm oil, tallow, rosin oil or 'green oil'. Green oil was a residue produced from the production of Lignole. More variants were obtained by blending 25% water with the tar instead of the caustic soda solution, and again adding 5 – 10% of vegetable or animal grease or oil. This produced a 'soft adhesive substance admirably adapted for lubricating purposes'. This addition of water to tar sounds odd, but the tar produced from peat is not the same as the tar produced from coal or oil. It mixes with water under the right conditions to form a stable substance.

Having found other markets for the peat tar, Henry didn't sit back; there was more to come. In the world of marine transport there were big changes in progress as the construction of ship's hulls changed from using wood to using iron. Traditionally, wooden hulls had been treated in order to prevent fouling by barnacles etc, by sheathing the hull with copper sheet, which also protected the timbers. With iron hulls this method of anti-fouling presented a major problem; placing two different metals in contact within salt water increases corrosion, in this instance corrosion of the iron. Alternatives were sought and in the 1840s, anti-fouling paints were developed. Although these paints were relatively easy to apply, they were unpleasant materials to handle, containing poisonous substances such as antimony, mercury, copper and arsenic. In August 1863, the Liverpool Echo reported that many anti-fouling mixtures which the Board of Admiralty had trialed had proved to be 'failures in possessing in anything like a complete degree, the two main essentials in an invention of this kind, viz, the property of preventing the growth of marine incrustations on iron ships' bottoms and of preserving the iron itself from the destructive chemical action of the water.' If an anti-fouling paint could be successfully produced to meet the Admiralty's requirements, it would also produce a fortune for the manufacturer.

Quite who or what directed Caunter to investigate the anti-fouling properties of peat tar is a mystery but, with the help of a Highland mariner – Captain James MacDonald – Caunter found what he was looking for. Peat tar did produce an excellent anti-fouling paint and a month after he had filed for another patent to protect this discovery, in December 1864, the Glasgow Herald stated:

> Mr Caunter discovered that the product of the distillation of peat possessed qualities of still greater value – having found, as we are informed, by an actual experiment that it acts as an excellent preventative of the fouling of ships' bottoms, successfully resisting those marine encrustations, whether of a vegetable

or animal nature, so detrimental and injurious to shipping. The naval gentleman (well known in the West Highlands) who took the trouble of making the experiment reports that at the end of six weeks the side of one of his vessels (a schooner) to which it was applied, presented the same clean appearance as when laid on, whilst the other side, on which he put the usual composition, became fouled as to require cleaning twice in that time. This discovery, we understand, has been covered by a patent.

Six months later, on 23rd May 1865, Caunter was granted Letters Patent for his invention (No 2985).

Caunter's enthusiasm for his new-found miracle substance knew no bounds. Besides the invention of an anti-fouling paint, the patent also covered the invention of the peat tar as a 'Preservative from the effects of Moisture and Damp' and as a 'Cure or Preventative of the Scab in sheep and as a protection to them from Damp'. It was almost as if Caunter was painting everything – animate or inanimate – with his peat tar to monitor the effect.

The production of the preservative was similar to that of the lubricant; the tar was simply mixed with 25% water in a mixing mill. Depending on the temperature at which the preservative was to be used, vegetable or mineral oils were added rather than water. The composition was applied hot or cold with a brush or the object could be immersed. When used as a sheep dip, a small amount of soda was added to the preservative.

In October 1865, Henry Caunter gave a guided tour of the Creed and Garrabost works to the Skye correspondent of the Inverness Courier who, on 9th November 1865, waxed lyrical regarding the scene at the Creed: '[an] extraordinary number of peat stacks arranged on both sides of an iron tramway on which wagons are placed and filled, and then hauled to the works by steam power. When the wind is favourable sails are set on the wagons to hasten their progress.'

On visiting Garrabost, he commented on the production of the paraffin: 'Here paraffin oil is produced in immense quantities, and paraffin itself [wax], in appearance somewhat like frosted snow. It is sent off to London to be made into candles, that being the only place where such candles are made.'

Interestingly, the correspondent also gives an indication of the state of development of the works as not yet being a fully operational commercial venture:

> As a mechanical and chemical experiment, the matter, I believe, may be considered to have completely succeeded and it is now on its trial as a commercial speculation, and considering the very great amount of mind as well as money that has been expended upon the process involved, it is to be wished that it may succeed as a manufacturing and commercial speculation also.

Caunter impressed the correspondent as an able, knowledgeable and patient guide and manager and the man who was also 'constructor of the works'. There was no mention of Benjamin Paul or Donald Morison!

Six months after being granted his patent, Caunter launched the 'The Lews Anti-Fouling Grease (Caunter's Patent)', which was advertised for sale in the Glasgow Herald on 13th December 1865: 'This preparation is found to be completely efficacious in Preventing the Fouling of Ship's and Boat's Bottoms, whether of Wood or Iron, besides greatly improving their rate of sailing.'

The grease was sold at £28 per ton together with directions for use and testimonials of efficacy, available from Messrs Lemmuel, Goddard and Finch in London. It could also be purchased directly from the Lewis Chemical Works which, would-be customers were reminded, had a regular steam communication with Glasgow. The advert ran daily for a week. Morison notes that the testimonials had been obtained after samples of the grease had been sent to several ports, notably Liverpool where, after much testing of the product, a ship's chandler gave an order for the entire output of the works and at a good price.

The future of the Lewis Chemical Works seemed to be assured as far as James Matheson was concerned. People were employed on the island in making a variety of products from peat for ready markets, under the supervision of an enthusiastic manager who was an old and trusted friend. But there was yet more to come.

In 1864 James Young's patent on the refining of tar ran out and other companies soon began to exploit the oil shale of the Lothians. Safety was a major feature in the marketing of these burning oils because of the availability of cheap but dangerous American oils. Paul had made much of the high flash-point of Lignole in his 1862 adverts in the Glasgow Herald.

One Bathgate shale oil manufacturer noted that adding peat tar to shale oil when it was distilled produced a paraffin with a higher flash-point. A higher flash-point meant higher returns in the competitive market and a favourable offer was made for the Lewis peat tar.

Curiously, Caunter did not take up this offer; instead he had been sent off on a tangent by a German visitor to the Creed works who arrived in 1865 with written permission (from whom it is not known) to study the works. Germany had a thriving peat distillation industry at that time, with peat deposits near Hannover, Osnabruck and Coburg, worked to produce paraffin. Samples of German paraffin oil had been exhibited at the International Exhibition of 1862 held in London. Morison's chiding description of the German industry – most likely gleaned from Caunter's tales of his earlier trip there – was probably in marked contrast to the situation as it existed in Germany, although it caused an amusing incident: 'Next day he [the German chemist] came alone Minutely examining the Works, expressed admiration for the arrangement of the whole was bluntly asked, If that was not better than Empty Herring Barrels as at the German Peat Works.'

The German's wit being no match for Lewis humour, he retreated to his native tongue: '[He] appeared startled and gave a long answer in German, to which he was replyed to in Gaelic which put us both on the same level. He departed with more information than Dr Paul and Mr Caunter got at the German Peat Works.'

Morison also sceptically suggested that the chemist was trying to obtain dyes – specifically indigo blue – from peat tar. The 1860s were part of what became known as the Mauve Decade (1857-1867), when the world was treated to an explosion in the availability of artificial dyes and which saw the establishment of the modern dye industry. Previously dyers had needed to rely on naturally occurring dyes – alizarin for red and indigo for blue, both of which were extracted from plants grown in the Far East. A natural purple dye was made from a Mediterranean shellfish, very scarce and expensive and so associated with royalty.

One of the most serendipitous discoveries that arose from the investigation of coal tar was made by eighteen year old William Perkin in 1856. Perkin, whilst trying to synthesise the anti-malarial drug quinine, discovered a purple dye, named mauve by the French dyers. Other colours such as magenta soon followed as the world of fashion was lit up, and young Perkin made a fortune. Paul had mentioned to Morison the possibility of extracting dyes from peat tar and had plans to do so, although indigo blue was not in his thinking. Paul reckoned the German chemist was a spy when he was informed about it on his return to the island as a visitor.

This colour craze would have appealed to Caunter's taste and the chance of extending the palette of paints would offer fresh, exciting possibilities to the artistic world. The possibility of actually making a dye had Henry fired up; if dyes came from coal tar why not also from peat tar? The German chemist and Dr Paul both seemed to think it was possiblle and Henry was no chemist to argue. After the visit of the foreigner, Henry set to work once more as Morison relates: 'Having occation to Visit the Refinery with Mr Caunter, I was shown Experiments going on to manufacture Indigo Blue. On a table, about 15 pacers [test-tubes] with wisps of Wool yarn etc steeped in some Mixture, several of the Wisps had a Tint of Blue. All now wanted was the Missing Link.'

The ancient alchemists used to search for the 'Philosopher's Stone' to enable them to convert metals into gold. Henry, the latter day alchemist, was now searching for the 'missing link' to convert peat tar into dye and so make the production of indigo blue another feature of the Lewis Chemical Works – thereby turning peat into gold. A third patent looked like a possibility and Caunter was keen to let the world know. On 13th January 1866 the London Evening Standard ran a brief note reporting that an indigo dye had been extracted from peat tar at the chemical works of Sir James Matheson in Stornoway. A few days later, on 16th January, the John O'Groat Journal ran a more upbeat article:

Readers already familiar with the brilliant dyes extracted from the chemical products of coal tar and the refuse of gas works, which under the names of mauve and magenta, etc have become so valuable and so common. We believe that a dye of similar nature, but of an indigo colour, has been eliminated from the products of peat distillation at the works established in the Lewis by the enterprising Sir James Matheson for the manufacture of paraffine. The discovery is considered to have important utilitarian and economical results and we believe, will be secured by a patent.

Buoyed by his discoveries and successful patents, Caunter came up with a development plan in the spring of 1866. He decided to build a new works for the distillation of peat 'to be Built within ½ a Mile from the Refinery'. It is doubtful however that this new works was built to increase the output of peat tar in order to meet all the demands of the anti-fouling, the grease and the shale oil industries on the mainland and of the Garrabost refinery on Lewis. The Creed works were functioning well and producing more tar than could be worked up. Four days after the building of the new works was commenced, the Creed works was forced to close temporarily; there were sixty-five tons of tar waiting for treatment and the storage vats were full. Maybe Caunter saw a chance to rectify the 'Enormous, Reckless, Blunder' of Paul's haphazard planning. The only reason Morison could discern for a new works was the search for the 'missing link' to make the indigo blue. He credited the notion for the new works to Caunter's state of mind during a period in which Caunter was confined to Glen House for four weeks with an attack of gout, to which he regularly succumbed.

At any rate Caunter submitted his plans and estimates to Matheson who listened and being a man of action, eventually granted him £1,600: 'Mr Caunter must have applied his power of Persuading on the *NOBLE* Sir *JAMES* before he granted him the sum of £1,600, which to finish would require £2,000.'

Morison is scathing in his condemnation of Caunter, full of outrage at his ignorance and lack of business and engineering abilities: 'There was not the Shadow of reason for the New Work. Its Plan and Condencing apparatus was as Impractable as can be emagined. Here £1,600 of Sir James Matheson's Money flung away. The result of the infatuation and want of decerment of H.Caunter, Esq, Manager of the L.C.Works.'

On 21st May 1866, construction of the new works started but they were never completed, and were eventually demolished as Morison sombrely related: '[the works] stood as a sticked Job for several years. Demolished. The bricks sold, Condensers broke up, sold as scrap iron, The Engene and Boiler brought to the Patent slip saw Mill.'

The location of these works is somewhat speculative but there is compelling evidence for one particular site. Adjacent to the Garrabost Mill, which lies about a quarter of a mile from the site of the Glen stills (the Knock Works), is the mill kiln where, until the closure of the mill a couple of years ago, the grain was dried over a peat fire in preparation for grinding into flour. The mill was built in 1893 but the kiln was not built until some years later; in the late 1890s according to Graham Morrison. The large scale O.S. map of 1897 shows only a regular rectangular recess into the banking where the kiln was subsequently built.

The kiln is a simple brick shed, originally roofed with tiles, all the building materials being of local manufacture. A floor of perforated iron plates stands about six feet off the ground, supported by brick work and iron beams. Beneath is a tunnel for a peat fire. This drying floor is accessed by steps on either side of the hearth entrance. The grain was spread on the iron plates and heat from the fire rose up through the grain which was occasionally turned as it dried.

A curious feature lies in the floor, just outside the hearth, yet partially built over by the bottom step of the left-hand stair leading up to the drying floor. This is a cast-iron plate, about four feet square, with a rectangular hole about 15" x 30" symmetrically offset from the centre, the whole plate being flush with the concrete floor. The plate has strengthening ridges and reinforced holes cast into the corners, as well as other symmetrically placed square and round holes. The plate seems to serve no purpose as far as the drying of the grain or the operation of the simple hearth are concerned. Its position – under the step – would indicate that it was already in situ when the drying kiln was constructed.

Caunter's new works would have required a level site with a concrete floor pan and nearby water supply for the steam engine and condensers which formed part of his plan. The concrete floor pan of the kiln house may be the remnants of such a site, just a few metres from the stream, Allt nan Gall, which provided water for the Garrabost Mill. The 1897 O.S. map, dating from before the kiln was built, shows a straight-edged, right-angled area cut into the nearby banking, but marked as a gravel pit. Such a situation would have provided a site close to the probable route of a track leading down to the stills in the Glen, essential for access from the main road.

When the new works were demolished, the concrete floor pan, together with its inlaid cast-iron plate, would have remained and provided an ideal base on which to build the drying kiln. Given this scenario, perhaps the complex design of the plate suggests that it was the mounting bed for the steam engine or some other piece of the apparatus that formed part of Caunter's new works.

Another feature of the drying kiln adds to the mystery. The tunnel in which the peat fire burned, providing the drying draught for the grain, was created using a piece of hemi-cylindrical cast iron, about six feet long. It is unlikely that such an expensive, bespoke fitting would have been used specifically for such a simple kiln design; it just probably happened to be available as scrap metal lying around the site, perhaps either from the Knock works in the Glen or from Caunter's new works, and was put to good use as with the previously mentioned possible condenser cap.

While Caunter was busy developing his new works, Donald Morison was also busy throughout the summers of the late 1860s, developing a new product. The increasing demand for coal by the factories and transport systems was not being met by the supply chain; prices were going up and availability was going down as mine-owners and miners bargained. The 'coal famine' as it was known, lasted from the early 1860s to the 1870s. The search for alternatives to coal was on and, by 1874, there were well over 100 patents filed for converting peat into charcoal, peat-coal and lamp oil, as fuels suitable for steam engines and domestic use.

Over the summers of 1866-68, Morison produced a simple method of producing what he termed 'Improved Peat Fuel or Coal'. This involved mashing the raw peat in a wooden mould and forming the mashed peat into peat-sized pieces which were dried in the same way as normal peats. The mashing of the peat, using heavy wooden beaters, broke up the plant fibres and allowed the peat to dry very quickly – the peats so formed could be lifted in just four days. The fuel burned well, was dust-free and of a smaller bulk than normal peat but whether it reached the markets is not known.

By the time the new works was started, MacFadyen and his co-workers had managed to re-establish the production of Lignole lighting oil and the selling price had gradually fallen from the 1862 price of 3s 6d (17½p) to 2s (10p) per gallon. In 1867, Caunter re-launched the whole enterprise – albeit without indigo dyes – with an advert in the 1867 Post Office Annual Glasgow Directory. The advert detailed a comprehensive list of products available from 'The Lewis Chemical Works, the Property of Sir James Matheson, Bart', the works being presented as an industrial complex covering various sites: 'Creed Works, Knock Works – Pitch, Grease and Crude Oil Distilleries. Garrabost Works – Grease, Oil and Paraffin etc, Refinery'.

The 'LEWS' brand of products was impressive:

> THE LEWS PATENT ANTI-FOULING
> GREASE, for Ships Bottoms etc
>
> THE LEWS PATENT LUBRICATING
> GREASE, for Gearing , Wheels etc
>
> THE LEWS ANTI-CORROSIVE PASTE, for
> Polished Metal Surfaces
>
> THE LEWS CRYSTALLIZED PARAFFIN
> WAX, Crude and Refined
>
> THE LEWS CAULKING PITCH, Various
> Sorts
>
> THE LEWS 'LIGNOLE' or NON-
> EXPLODING PARRAFIN OIL
>
> THE LEWS CREOSOTE – SULPHATE OF
> SODA, PEAT CHARCOAL etc.

The selling agent was Messrs M Parker and Co. of 90 Mitchell Street, Glasgow.

The Valuation Roll of 1865 indicates that the lease on the Lewis Chemical Works – valued at £30 – was for fifty-seven years or upwards; the plan was that the works were there for the long run. It had taken ten years, but Matheson's hopes for Lewis were being realised and all that remained for success was for the markets to respond and for the Works to run smoothly, without major upset.

Chapter Ten

A *Spanner in the Works*

'and the eyes of ages watch our tinsel show,
while hireling wages steal our dreams from our souls.
minarets of industry
spinnarets of alchemy
colonnades of chemistry
and cavalcades of conjury'
– from 'Tinsel Show' by Karine Polwart

Whilst Henry Caunter was busy creating new products for the markets, filing for patents, dabbling with dyes and generally trying to manage the running of the works, James MacFadyen found himself in changed circumstances from those of his post under Dr Paul. Caunter had provided MacFadyen with a position of security, although MacFadyen had placed himself in an uncertain role with respect to his ability to carry out the refining. Security, together with uncertainty heightens opportunity, which soon became apparent to the clever brickmaker. In this case an opportunity to develop his own business plan.

According to Morison, MacFadyen started his own money making schemes soon after Paul left the works in April 1862. MacFadyen's plan was very simple – to supply the local market with paraffin oil. What probably started off as part of the retail stream of the Lewis Chemical Works became MacFadyen's own enterprise for a number of years, as Morison related: 'It maybe Noticed that after Dr Paul left, the Lignoulene (Lamp oil) was sold at the Refinery to the Vilages Both sides of the Broad Bay.'

This was a large market. Paul had kept meticulous records of the tar transferred between the Creed works and the Garrabost refinery, which Caunter continued, producing a monthly statement of the tar transported. MacFadyen made sure that the paper chase soon ended, as the Lignole was sold 'in Bottles, Gallons, and Casks. CASH SALES without any CHECK.'

Soon after he was appointed as chemist at the refinery, MacFadyen's family and his friends – notably his brother Hugh – arrived to join him, no doubt aware that there were rich pickings to be made. Morison refers to them as MacFadyen's 'associates' or the 'Irish Clique'. What allowed MacFadyen and his associates to operate for six years without their deception coming to light was their ability to manipulate Caunter, who was putty in their hands, seduced by their blarney and pumped up by their flattery: 'Caunter being under the influence of MacFaden and his associates, and of such a credulous disposition and without the sagacity to decern his being led by the clique at the refinery.'

Caunter himself was not accountable to any board. There were no regular management meetings as there were with Matheson's gas and water companies. In fact the Lewis Chemical Works was never registered as a company. It appears to have been Matheson and Caunter's own project, with Caunter responsible only to Matheson, although neither seems to have realised this. Alas, events would show that Caunter was unable to live up to one of Matheson's guiding business principles: 'I disapprove of reserve in business matters there being nothing so conducive to a good understanding as the most perfect frankness and the free disclosure of even disagreeable truths.'

Although the verbal charms of the clique prevented Caunter from realising the lying and stealing that was taking place at Garrabost, others knew. Morison himself was aware that things were not right and George Craig, the work's cooper at the refinery, was dismissed for 'daring to take notice of the dishonesty at the refinery.'

This sacking begs the question, who was responsible for dismissing Craig? Morison is ruled out as he had no managerial authority and was above suspicion. Had Caunter been made aware of any dishonesty he would have reacted in a positive way; it would not have been in his interest to allow such dishonesty to proceed. The only other person with the power to hire and fire (besides Matheson, who remained aloof from such matters) was the factor, Donald Munro, and to oppose him required daring. According to Morison, Munro was not impressed by MacFadyen: 'Donald Munro, Factor to Sir James to show his displeasure at what he called the Irish Colony of MacFadens and Friends employed on several occasions sent their pay in a separate bag.'

Perhaps MacFayden himself was given the authority to hire and fire as part of his managerial responsibility at the refinery. Local labour would be hired when needs required – peat cutting etc – and just as easily fired.

In 1874 – the year that the Lewis Chemical Works closed – the hated Donald Munro was dismissed for his shameful deeds. These involved irregular financial doings. All this makes compelling evidence for the conspiracy

199

theorist that MacFadyen and Munro were in league; perhaps it was not just a coincidence that the works and Munro fell simultaneously.

The development of the Lewis Chemical Works and the diversification of products must have delighted Caunter, whose remit as manager was to further Matheson's aim of providing employment and to exploit the natural resources of Lewis. The production of the anti-fouling grease and other greases could easily be carried out at the Creed works, but the Garrabost refinery was essential for the production of Lignole. As the demand for the various greases increased, less peat tar was finding its way out to Garrabost for refining. Essentially, the peat tar was being sold directly from the Creed works. This created a frustrating problem for James MacFadyen; that of supply and demand. The local demand for lighting oil hadn't changed, but the supply of the necessary peat tar had fallen. MacFadyen needed to divert more of the tar from the Creed works to the Garrabost refinery and for this he had a plan.

He first dealt with the tar used for making lubricants. Caunter's first patent (No. 1678) covered the manufacture of grease, made by treating the tar with caustic soda solution and mineral or vegetable oil. Six months later, in December 1863, Caunter was granted a second patent (No. 3290) which extended 1678 by using water rather than caustic soda solution to form a different lubricant. This involved adding about 25% water to the tar and blending the two liquids in a mill (triturating or macerating). This mixing of tar and water sounds counter-intuitive but probably produced a stable emulsion in much the same way olive oil and vinegar can be made to mix permanently as salad cream, if there is some egg-yolk present. Morison appears only to have been aware of the first patent: 'The Lubricating Grease had a percentage of

Green Oil [a by-product from the refinery] mixed with it But no water.'

MacFadyen discovered that using a large proportion of water produced a relatively stable substance. This grease, made with nearly three times the amount of water required by the patent, was presented to the impressionable Caunter: 'James MacFadyen and his associates at the Refinery began to Experiment, Made Mr Caunter to believe that 2/3 by measure of water added to the Tar would improve the grease.' By effectively 'diluting' the grease with water, MacFadyen was skimming off peat tar for Lignole production, boosting his own schemes.

The mixture of peat tar and water would be stable for a while but, as olive oil and vinegar in salad dressing eventually reform into two layers, the water would eventually separate out from the grease. Morison was not keen to prepare the grease in such a way, probably fearing the outcome. For Caunter it was a matter of not losing face. Morison eventually carried out Caunter's wishes when the latter pulled rank. The subsequent partial separation of the tar still did not deter the stubborn Caunter from despatching a large order to Glasgow with the inevitable result:

> He seeing our hesitate to make this Mixture and reminded by him that he was Manager, Stood over the adding of the Water to 3 Tons which was put in Casks. Sent to Glasgow to fulfil an order. The 3 Tons of Grease Mixed under Mr Caunter's Personal superentendance Was ordered to be carted to Steamer next day. When it was descovered that the Tar and Water had partley seperated and in a crudely state. When appealed to against sending it in that State in Vain, He would have it off. With the

Result of its return from Glasgow by return of
Steamer and no more ordered.

MacFadyen was playing Caunter at his own game – baffling
him with science waffle – a ploy which he continued to use
to increase the flow of tar to Garrabost.

Caunter's anti-fouling grease was proving popular and
profitable and it was easier to make than the lubricating
grease as the anti-fouling manufacture required no
additional chemicals to be added to or react with the tar.
This allowed James MacFadyen to come up with a simple
ruse to divert tar. He proposed that the refining of the tar
had an advantageous effect on its use as an anti-fouling
grease. He painted some pieces of iron with tar that had
been partially distilled. After a week of being immersed in
the sea, the metal appeared unchanged. MacFadyen then
showed these samples of metal and the bogus results to
Caunter and in his sweet talking way, successfully persuaded
the gullible man that the metal had been left submerged
for six months, rather than a week, and that the distilling
of the tar had improved the quality of the anti-fouling
grease:

> MacFadan and associates began to Experiment,
> and Convinced Mr Caunter That by parcially
> distilling the Tar it would improve the Anti-
> fouling Grease. Pieces of Iron placed under
> water in the Broad Bay. In a week took up to
> the Works Made Mr Caunter believe the Iron
> lay coated for 6 Months under water, covered
> with Tar partly distilled appeared clean from
> Fouling. Any Trick to prevent the Tar being
> sold direct from Creed was the Sole Aim of The
> MacFadens and associates.

Ever eager for improvements, Caunter sent the tar to the refinery for MacFadyen to distil. MacFadyen produced more Lignole and the remnants of the distillation were dispatched 'south' (to the Liverpool chandlers or to London, where a distributor was based) as genuine anti-fouling. Again, orders were stopped when the grease was found to be unusable: 'This [the experiment] causing the Tar to be sent to the Refinery to be Distilled, the residue, of Tuff Pitch sent south as Anti-Fouling Grease which resulted in the stoping of orders.'

MacFadyen's ability to manipulate Caunter seemed total. Not only could he produce evidence and persuasive reasoning on which Caunter would act, he could also contrive a situation to keep Caunter's mind occupied with matters that kept him away from the underhand goings-on at the refinery. While Caunter was excitedly experimenting, chasing the 'missing link' in the production of indigo blue dye, traces of blue colour were appearing in his test tubes which gave him hope and encouragement that the extraction of the dye should be possible. He just needed to keep experimenting. Unbeknownst to the hapless man however, his researches were being sabotaged by MacFadyen: 'Mr Caunter in GREAT GUSTO, Great discovery to be Made. It USED out that unknown to him a real Blue was added by the clique to keep him in Trim.' It was MacFadyen, as part of this deception, who sowed the seeds in Henry's mind that were later to germinate as the abortive new works that kept Caunter occupied for long enough.

There still remained the question of the potential loss of the entire Lignole production as a result of the offer from the Lothian shale works, to take the peat tar directly from the Creed works. MacFadyen simply planted an unpalatable fear in Caunter's mind which Caunter later revealed to Morison: 'Mr Caunter honestly admitted That his reason for refusing to sell the Peat Tar to the Shale Oil Works was That it would be an admission of his inability to refine it at Home, and put the Refinery Idle after being fitted up at Great Expense.'

While Caunter was distracted with his dyes and his new works, MacFadyen's wholesale deceit went on unnoticed by his manager. According to Morison, MacFadyen started his dealings in 1862, then, as he found he could get away with things, he became bolder. His schemes to bring more tar to Garrabost probably started some time in 1866 as the adverts for anti-fouling grease did not appear in the press until late December 1865. The grand deception continued throughout 1867 and it was not until Caunter had an attack of gout in February 1868, which led to a chance visit to the refinery, where he discovered the mayhem and treachery.

Matheson had put a lot of money and faith in Henry Caunter's abilities but Caunter was involved up to his neck with responsibilities that put him well out of his comfort zone. His ego was fragile and vulnerable and he was moved to tears, which soon gave way to anger, as the financial consequences of the chaos for which he was responsible became apparent. Well over £3,000 had been either lost, stolen or wasted. His brooding fury at MacFadyen and his gang was boosted by his own sense of self-righteous indignation. Morison is at his most animated in describing these events and his concise, compressed style highlights the passions aroused. Once again Morison was Caunter's sounding-board and soothsayer:

> Mr Caunter altho a Heavely robust Bodied Gentleman, was a marter to GOUT in his Feet. Had a prolonged attack in Feby 1868 which Confined him to his House for 10 days. On calling on him shortly after his return from

his first visit to the Refinery after his recovery, I found him in Great distress *ACTUALLY SHEDING TEARS* Caused as he Confessed by the State he found those in Charge at the Refinery on his (by them) unexpected Visit, all incapable with *DRINK*, a large quantity of Parafine Wax destroyed and unsaleable. *HONESTLY CONFESSED WITH TEARS* That he did not know or could account for but a small percentage of the Lignoline (Lamp Oil) Distilled from all the Tar received at the Refinery for the Last 12 Months. The oil Tanks in *STORE* supposed by him to be full of Finished refined Oil, Now discovered Empty. When Spoken to, was answered with Insolence by the MacFadens (a small colony of them having arrived after James got to be Chemist and the Refinery).

The Refinery's Monthly Pay Sheets was at hand on examining It was found that 320 Tons of Tar was Certified by J. MacFaden to have been received during the Year ending 31 January 1868 Which Cost at Creed Works £1130 add Carting, Chemicals etc at the Refinery. This distressing result as he said in his *OVERCONFIDENCE IN UNWORTHY MEN* and now his suspicion of foul dealing from first was confirmed. Asked for My Advice to him under this serious State of affairs in which he found himself Which I did in writing next Morning. Left him late at Night, Pouring out bolts of excommunication on the Irish Clique and Confederates, the whole lot was to be Cleared of Bag and Baggage from the Refinery. A Chemist was to be got as should at First. This Burst of anger led to a relapse of Gout which Kept him in his room for other 8 Days.

Morison did indeed write to Caunter, a forthright but respectful letter full of home truths, empathy and advice but also a little remorse, reminding Caunter of his own sacrifices to support Henry:

Creed Gate House

1ˢᵗ March 1868

H. Caunter Esq, Dear Sir, sorry for your distress. The result of misplaced confidence in Men who from the first took advantage of the trust you gave them to enrich themselves being by you allowed for 6 years to supply the Villages both sides of Broad Bay and other places with Parafine oil. Cash sales at the Works without Check. See how they got you to upset the Lubricating and Anti-fouling Grease and again to refuse the sale of Tar direct from Creed to the Bathgate Shale Works and again to spend £1600 on a work not required. Which stands as an unfinished monument of imposition on a confining Nature etc. My advice to you is to confess your descovery yesterday to D. Munro who will serch into the affair and dismiss the whole pack, Advertise for a Chemist to take charge in place of those who never should have been in charge of what was so important To Sir James Matheson, Bt, yourself and the Whole Estate, and not less to me who gave up promising situations at my Trade for the L. C.

Works at which I got engrafted by the Advise of Sir James Matheson and his Factor after Dr B. H. Paul left the works. Yours etc D. Morison

Copy rendered on Date

P.S. You asking my advice last night will I hope excuse my freedom.

Caunter must have done some hard thinking whilst laid up in Glen House with gout. It is not known if he did indeed confess all to Donald Munro as Donald Morison had advised, but in the light of subsequent events, it seems unlikely. If Caunter had so acted there would have been a good chance that Matheson would have become aware of the shambles that had been allowed to develop and with it the derailment of his precious schemes. If Donald Munro had been told, the fact that he did not fire MacFadyen – who did survive along with his associates – would add to the conspiracy theory that Munro and MacFadyen were indeed in cahoots.

A week after the terrible revelation, Caunter hitched up his pony and trap and headed back to the Garrabost refinery. Donald Morison was present at the meeting between Caunter and the workforce, but only related the result, which was that surprisingly, after much soul-searching and flattery, everyone kept their jobs. Morison described the emotional scenes at the refinery using a literary analogy from Thomas Carlyle's *Past and Present*, in which rebellious monks are brought to task by a temperate, reserved and strict, but devoted abbot – Abbot Samson – now cast as Henry Caunter: 'When first able to Drive to the Refinery, The Humbling of the St Edmund Monks to Abbot Samson was acted over again.'

The passage from *Past and Present* is quoted by Morison almost verbatim, although the spelling and emphases are his own, which suggests that it was quoted from memory. The emotional scene must have had quite an impact on Morison:

> We decide on humbling ourselves before the Abbot, by word and gesture in order to Medigate [mitigate] his mind. He replying with much humelety, Yet alleging his own justice turning the blame on us. When he saw us conquered, *HIMSELF CONQUERED* – swore that he never was greaved so much for anything, First for himself and Cheafley for the *SCANDAL* which had gone abroad – Embraced all of us – *HE WEPT, WE WEPT*, What a picture. Behaved better ye remiss Monks, and thank Heaven for such an Abbot – or Know that ye must and shall obey.

So the refinery weathered the storm and full production was resumed with Caunter at the helm, MacFadyen behaving at Garrabost and Donald Morison keeping the whole show on the road at Creed works. This *ménage-a-trois* did not last long. Caunter probably kept a tight rope on MacFadyen and the clique and they were soon on the move looking for other plunder. In 1869, James MacFadyen and family set sail for America to further their fortunes in the opportunities provided by the Wild West as Morison related, with more than a hint of irony as to their benefactor for such a venture: 'Next year [1869] James and Famely left for America Where they Bought Farms, and no doubt Blessing their stars for having met with such a Confining Gentleman as Henry Caunter Esquire Manager of the L. C. Works Refinery.'

Caunter was perhaps deflated by MacFadyen's antics but he was not beaten yet. Morison was once more confounded as his advice to hire a chemist was ignored by Caunter, who amazingly appointed James MacFadyen's brother, Hugh, to the post. Hugh, who had moved to Garrabost some six or seven years previously as a flower pot maker, was now in charge of the Garrabost refinery.

Sadly, due in part to the interference of James MacFadyen, the apparent potential of the Lewis Chemical Works was never to be realised. Years later, Donald Morison was quite unequivocal about who to blame as he described MacFadyen's promotion to works chemist that evening in Glen House: 'Thus on the evening of the 22nd April 1862, the ruinous failure of the Lewis Chemical Works was pronounced in Glen House. H Caunter Esq and James MacFadyen to take the place of Dr B. Paul.'

But, just as the works appeared to be free of disruption and the future looked hopeful, there were other more powerful, irresistible forces at work, forces which were to bring about the downfall of the Lewis Chemical Works within a few short years.

Chapter Eleven

The Fires Go Out

'... success seems to have been a mixture of one
part of expertise to ten each of ingenuity, necessity
and hard graft in the most extreme conditions.'
– David Crabbe: former lecturer in Technology
at the Open University

Advertising for the Lews Brand products available from the
Lewis Chemical Works continued for 1868 and 1869 and
into the 1870s. Ever trying a new angle to catch the
competitive market in lighting oil, Caunter's Lignole was
also named Northern Light and was deemed to be 'Perfectly
safe from the danger of explosion to which all other Paraffin
Oils are liable.' It was a bold claim indeed but by this time
there was severe pressure on the home-produced lighting
oil, caused by the availability of cheap imported American
oil. In 1864, the Scottish oil industry was producing about
5.5 million gallons of oil per year from shale compared to
about thirty million gallons of imported US oil. By 1867,
Scottish output had reduced to less than a third of its 1864
production and the price of imported US oil had also reduced

to a third of its 1864 price. The Pennsylvania 'Oilocracy' was the economic powerhouse dictating the market.

In November 1867, in his introductory address to the Glasgow Philosophical Society, the president, Frances H. Thomson, chose as his topic the state of the Scottish oil industry. The depressed price of US oil had put Scottish producers 'virtually out of the field' and at the time of his address he reckoned that 'most of the Scottish refineries are at a stand still.' This was in stark contrast to the picture painted by a Glasgow Herald correspondent just two years previously, when in November and December of 1865, the paper ran a series of leading articles entitled 'Petrolia', describing in detail the state of the shale oil industry and the process of oil production which, the correspondent argued, had a bright future. However, Thomson had a plan to boost home sales.

The home market in America was also having problems with low grade paraffin causing dangerous explosions in oil lamps and during storage. To prevent this, US legislation had raised the flash point of the paraffin from 100°F (38°C) to 110°F (44°C) with severe financial and custodial sanctions for any who tried to deal in adulterated oils. The lower grade American oil, for which there was no home market, was simply exported to the UK where unscrupulous dealers used it to adulterate good paraffin to make it go further, while responsible refiners simply distilled off the objectionable naphtha – basically petrol – to leave good paraffin. The low grade US oil was unacceptable in other European countries.

Thomson suggested that the UK should match the US legislation and raise the legal flash point to 110°F (the US legislation did not apply to oil sold outwith America). He also recommended inspection of storage facilities and of the oil itself so that the paraffin did indeed comply with a higher flash point – a major problem with the then current legislation.

By spring 1868, opposition to US imports was gathering pace and petitions were being presented to Parliament by interested merchants and consumer groups in favour of an Oil Act Amendment Bill. A Parliamentary Select Committee of the House of Commons was taking evidence and in June 1868, the Glasgow Herald reported on the third reading of the Petroleum Act Amendment Bill. The Committee recommended adoption of the 110°F flash point limit 'to raise people's expectation of safety'. Things progressed and the Bill became Law, but the Petroleum Act 1868 did not come into force until February 1st 1869. Sadly, it was much diluted from the Bill put before Parliament by the Select Committee.

Once again, paraffin and politics were to create an explosive mix. The MPs for Liverpool and Birkenhead were a powerful lobby for the US oil industry as the Glasgow Herald of February 13th 1869 reported in its leader: 'Through the influence of certain 'wire-pullers' hailing it is said from Liverpool and Birkenhead, and who were directly or indirectly interested in the importation of petroleum, the measure in question [Petroleum Bill] was so manipulated in the Home Office that it left the House of Commons much less valuable than when it was introduced'.

The two MPs had argued that the trade imports of oil would be restricted by the Bill, stifling the revival of the oil-refining industry in the UK by removing a cheap raw material. They managed to prevail and the 100°F flash point was kept, but licences for dealers and the inspection of storage and of the oil itself became mandatory.

The respectable Scottish paraffin refiners had nothing to fear from this Act since they produced paraffin from shale oil with a flash point of 140°F, for which no licence was required. It was the adulterated oils marketed by mischievous refiners that the new Act sought to challenge. Advocating the making of the best of a bad bargain, the Herald was concerned that interpretation and administration should be fairly carried out by a competent authority working to strict guidelines, for instance, the Weights and Measures Department.

All of this was eagerly followed by Henry Caunter who saw the new Act as a vehicle for boosting sales of Lignole. A few days after the article appeared in the Herald, on March 11th 1869, he put pen to paper and wrote to the newspaper, lamenting the failure to raise the flash point of paraffin to 110°F and cautioning the importance of strict, standard regulation: 'a uniform method of observing the flash point must be adhered to, otherwise it is quite evident that there will be no end of trouble and annoyance.'

Henry had learned the importance of strict regulation in all dealings with people the hard way! He continued by taking up the gauntlet for the Lewis Chemical Works, announcing that, while oil of flashpoint 140°F was:

> satisfactory, the Lews Lignole or non-explosive paraffin manufactured here [Stornoway] is guaranteed up to 190°F and is not infrequently proof against explosion to and considerably beyond 200°F...making it pre-eminently the safest paraffin in the world, while in point of illuminating power and freedom from smoke and smell in burning it is not surpassed by any hydro-carbon oil in the market. Oils of this high standard cannot be produced from coal, shale or petroleum but only *from peat*, the raw material from which I manufacture the Lignole.

Having made his point, Henry then proceeded to advertise freely: 'I need scarcely remark how well adapted these oils are for use in even the hottest climates; and further that they are specially fitted to mix with lighter [lower flashpoint] oils for the purpose of raising them above the standard required by the Act.'

Henry ended his letter with a copy of a scientific report – commissioned just days before his letter to the paper – from Fredrick Penny, Professor of Chemistry at the Andersonian University, Glasgow. Penny gave an accurate determination of the flashpoint of Lignole as 200°F and fully backed up Henry's claims regarding Lignole. The report subsequently appeared in adverts for Lignole.

Was there a hint of desperation in Henry's letter? Perhaps he could see the way things were moving. However, he would have been cheered when, just ten weeks later, HRH Prince Arthur made a surprise visit to Stornoway, coming ashore for a brief tour. The Mathesons were in London at the time but Donald Munro arranged the day's outing. The Royal party were welcomed by a large, enthusiastic Stornoway crowd and visited the Lewis Castle and Grounds and the Callanish Stones, spending time successfully landing salmon on the Blackwater River after lunch at the Garynahine Inn. On route, they toured the Lewis Chemical Works. The Prince was 'much pleased with the visit'.

Adverts for the Lews brand products were appearing less frequently and by 1871 only featured in adverts placed by the merchants and commission agents M. Parker & Co of Glasgow. The large Scottish shale oil refiners and the Pennsylvanian 'Oilocracy' slowly dominated the scene.

In 1880, John Calderwood addressed the National Association for the Promotion of Social Science and spoke of the 'Scotch Oil Fever' which raged between 1864 and 1872, when many small shale oil refineries appeared and then rapidly succumbed before petroleum competition on the one hand, and increased costs of shale oil on the other. Lignole might have been the Rolls-Royce of lighting oils as Caunter and Professor Penny maintained but, with the added burdens, firstly, of transport to and from Lewis of essential chemicals for the process and of the products themselves and, secondly, the difficulties of winning the dry peat, the economics were always going to be tricky to manage.

Unfortunately there are no production records as they were either lost, destroyed in the Stornoway Town Hall fire, or never existed. Unlike the Stornoway Water Works and Gas Works the concern was never registered as a company with all the accompanying legal requirements. There was only one 'shareholder' and he seemed quite happy to respond to every request for funding. Eventually, Matheson was to spend £33,000 on the Lewis Chemical Works, some eight percent of his total outlay and expenditure on Lewis and the equivalent of £3,500,000 in today's money. Financial returns on his investment were probably less important to Matheson at the time than any improvement that his largesse could bring about. There is no way of knowing the income generated by the sales of the various products but it can only be a small fraction of the investment. In 1866, the correspondent of the Glasgow Herald sounded a wise caution to would-be investors in the exciting days of Scotch Oil Fever: 'remember the sound advice of James Watt, the great engineer, never to invest more in any speculation than they [the traders] are prepared to lose.' Perhaps the fact that Matheson was prepared to lose a large sum of money was a reflection of his aims when he came to Lewis; he saw the investment in the project not just as a business investment, but as an investment in people.

By 1874, Matheson was an old man of seventy-eight, with only a few years left. He spent much time in France and probably lost interest in the Lewis Chemical Works and his 'anxiety' to promote science. The Lewis Chemical Works no longer had a place in the competitive market. The American imports had burst the bubble of the Scottish oil industry just as they were to do 150 years later when a consequence of the US fracking industry was a major slump in the price of North Sea crude oil. In 1874, the fires of the furnaces at Creed, at Knock and at Garrabost were allowed to die, the stills cooled as the trickle of paraffin and other oils ceased and the moorlands became silent, except for the sounds of nature and the domestic peat cutters. The steady beat of steam engines hauling trucks or working the stirring mechanisms of vats and feeding the presses gave way to the steady rhythms of the seasons as nature reclaimed her own.

The various works were dismantled and the iron sold for scrap. The tracks out in the moorland were lifted; some of the rail still exists and can be seen, used for decades as fence posts around the Marybank area of Stornoway and at Garrabost. James Shaw Grant, a font of local knowledge, once remarked: 'The field between the Cabarfeidh [hotel] and the County Hospital running up towards the Memorial was known in my youth as the Stile Park. The stile beside the gate consisted of three large iron boxes, broad at one end, narrower at the other, splayed one on top of the other. It was said, and I think correctly, that these iron boxes were retorts from the chemical works.'

The parks at Garrabost were polluted well into the twentieth century. Alasdair MacIver of Milngavie recalls as a boy picking up some black material – probably tar, 'which when lit burnt like a modern fire-lighter'. Now there are just scars in the ground where once dreams were chased, fortunes were fiddled and hopes were cherished. To sum up the venture of the Lewis Chemical Works concisely is difficult. Morison finished his tale of events with another literary flourish, quoting Dr Fletcher, Dean of Peterborough, who was present to describe the scene at the execution of Mary Queen of Scots: 'And so end the Queen's Enemies.' Despite his sense of injustice, his humour was never far away.

After all the excitement of the birth of the Lewis Chemical Works recorded in the press some fifteen years earlier, the project died with no passing mention, however its existence was worth a brief mention by William Black in his article 'A Glance at the Island of Lewis', published in Harpers Monthly magazine the year after the closure:

> near Stornoway is a small manufactory which [Sir James Matheson] had put up for the purpose of distilling an inflammable oil from peat: and the experiment had so far succeeded that a very clear and good oil could be produced for (I think) about three shillings a gallon, when the immense supplies afforded by the American petroleum springs crushed the project of sending the peat oil into the market.

David Crabbe, recently retired as a lecturer in Technology at the Open University, gives a rich, encompassing description of what, for him, is: 'one of the most enchantingly bizarre episodes of Scottish industrial history ... This [the remains] all serves as a lasting testament to an enterprising, pioneering scheme whose recipe for (partial) success seems to have been a mixture of one part of expertise to ten each of ingenuity, necessity and hard graft in the most extreme of conditions'.

Chapter Twelve

People Move On

'At this distance in time, geography,
technical progress and even culture, it is easy
to be critical, almost mockingly so in places, but for
the folk associated with the Lewis Chemical Works
it would have been a significant achievement of
great local importance.'
– David Crabbe

Much human endeavour had been spent over the previous
seventeen years on Matheson's schemes for developing peat.
What happened to those involved after the demise of the
Lewis Chemical Works in 1874?

Six months after Benjamin Paul left Lewis in the spring
of 1862, he read a paper at the meeting of the British
Association for the Advancement of Science, held that year
in Cambridge. His paper, entitled 'On the Manufacture of
Hydrocarbon Oils, Paraffin etc, from Peat', was subsequently
reported in Chemical News in November 1862. In the paper
Paul described the development, progress and business plan
of the Lewis Chemical Works together with the results and

achievements of his labours in the marketing of Lignole and the testing of lubricants. There is no acknowledgment of Sir James Matheson, Henry Caunter or Donald Morison but this was probably the case with formal papers of the time. A few weeks later Paul read a similar paper to the Society of Arts. These papers agree well with Morison's assessment of the venture and contain many facts and figures, production targets etc. Paul presented a second paper to the Society of Arts in the following spring in 1863, a year after leaving Lewis. This paper was concerned with the distillation of coal, tar and peat in general and was a wide-ranging read. Notably, the only reference Paul made to peat distillation was to the work of Rees Reece carried out ten years previously in Ireland rather than to his own three years' experience at the Lewis Chemical Works completed just a year earlier.

Paul's passions led him away from the cut and thrust of the commercial world of the chemical industry. Although he had written extensively about industrial chemistry, the Lewis Chemical Works remain his only practical experience in the field. After leaving Lewis, he returned to London where he set up business as a chemical consultant and analyst, returning to his first instincts in chemistry, with a practice in Fenchurch Street. From then on, although very busy, his imperatives were not so pressing.

Paul's interest in scientific writing and reporting continued. In 1863 he helped Henry Watts complete his *Dictionary of Chemistry*. In 1878, seeing the need in Britain for a text book suitable for technical colleges, schools and manufacturers, he produced *Industrial Chemistry*, a translation based on a German edition of a French work which he adopted and extended. He wrote reports on the Paris Exhibition of 1878 and the First International Exhibition held at Vienna in 1883. He continued his deep interest in fuels and was the main witness to give evidence to the Royal Commission on Coal Supply during the years of the 1860s known as the 'Coal Famine'.

As a consultant, his interests were wide and varied: the preservation of stone buildings; steel and steel production; sewage and its disposal and use; ventilation systems; artificial light; refrigeration and ice-making; patent litigation. He enjoyed the intellectual challenges of chemistry and was a keen scientific society man. In 1868, he was elected a life-member of the Chemical Society, becoming its Vice-president from 1891-94. In 1875, he became a member of the Society of Public Analysts; in 1880, a Fellow and council member of the Institute of Chemistry and in 1883, a member of the Society of Chemical Industry.

Alongside his consultancy, he developed his analytical skills at the bench and explored his interest in pharmacology, so much so that in 1870, he was appointed as the editor of the Pharmaceutical Journal – the organ of the Pharmaceutical Society which he had joined in 1852. He held the position for over three decades during which he influenced the direction and the development of the Society, retiring as the elder-statesman of pharmacology in 1902, aged seventy-three.

Paul wasn't just a committee man and reporter of science. With AJ Cownley in his laboratory, Paul investigated alkaloid drugs and became a world-renowned expert on epecacuanha and quinine, writing over fifty papers during his lifetime.

In 1870, he married Helena Katherine and they had a daughter, Helena, in 1874 and a son, Benjamin, in 1893. The latter was a serving officer in Salonica when, in November 1917, his father passed peacefully away whilst enjoying dinner at his home in Kingston Vale, Putney. He was eighty-nine. The Journal of the Chemical Society described him on his death as:

[the] last of the Olympians of the early epic years of the British scientific pharmacy. Dr Paul was an accomplished and versatile linguist, widely travelled with an intimate knowledge of Continental life and thought, a brilliant conversationalist, an artistic raconteur of remarkable histrionic power with a wonderful gift of playful and poignant wit, one of the most chivalrous and magnanimous of men, as ready to take a manly foeman to his arms as to break a lance with him.

His fellow pharmacist, R Broadbent, saw the more abrasive side to his character: 'I remember well how he strummed with his fingers as he rubbed in some caustic irony and his bantering tone as he laid bare the idiosyncrasies of those who dared to rush in where he feared not to tread.'

The columnist 'X-rayser' in the 'Chemist and Druggist' did not mince his words either when describing Paul's confrontational side: 'Dr Paul was not one to suffer fools gladly, but, in later years, he became less and less sarcastic and of the many who have crossed swords with him there is not but one who cherishes the most kindly thoughts of the grand old warrior.'

'The Pharmaceutical Journal', so long his mouthpiece, was fulsome in its praise: 'There is removed one of the last of the Olympians of British scientific pharmacy. His life pilgrimage, so full of years and honour, was for a long space of its course contemporaneous with the history and progress of the Society.'

The scientific literature, the scientific annals and the popular press recorded a life lived to the full, living his dream of discovering chemistry, eventually finding fulfilment in pharmacology, with a rewarding living and public service.

But nowhere – other than his BAAS paper of 1862 specifically on the subject – is there any mention of the Lewis Chemical Works. There is nothing during his lengthy retirement, nothing in his own writings and nothing in his obituary notices. It is almost as if something happened in Lewis that clouded his scientific work; something personal that he wanted to forget. The Lewis Chemical Works took up a big chunk of his formative years but it was a frustration as practical chemical engineering was Paul's Achilles Heel. Perhaps the oral tradition of Garrabost – the tale of the doctor departing the Garrabost brick works with a local girl – speaks of times and memories which Paul could not bear to recall.

Paul forgot Lewis but Lewis did not forget him and on the grazings of Garrabost to this day, in sight of the brickworks, there exists an area known locally as 'Garadh Pol' – Paul's enclosure – to remind the world of a most quixotic and prickly Victorian man of Chemistry.

While Benjamin Paul left Lewis for pastures new, Donald Morison spent the remainder of his days in the land of his birth. With the close of the Lewis Chemical Works, Donald took over responsibility for the Garrabost Brick Works and the family moved to Garrabost. When the brick-works shut sometime in the late 1880s, Donald and his wife, daughter and grandson moved back to the family house at Bayhead in Stornoway. Mary-Jane had married a Royal Navy diver/carpenter, Angus MacKay of 37 Lower Garrabost, who was at sea, and whose brother had been a tile-maker at the Garrabost Brick Works. Donald Morison continued his trade as a builder, working locally, which included providing a report for the Stornoway Harbour Commission on 'the contemplated improvements of the inner harbour wherein he [Donald Morison] estimates the cost at £740', as the Commission secretary minuted. The plans were drawn up by Donald's pal, Henry Caunter, for submission to the Board of Trade. Henry charged the Commission six guineas (£6.30) for his work whilst Donald charged one guinea (£1.05).

Morison kept up his interest in developments in the peat industry for the remainder of his life following the demise of the Lewis Chemical Works. In 1895 – the year he wrote his manuscript and two years before his death – he read about 'Blunden's process for manufacturing Peat Coal' in the magazine 'Land and Water'. The article referred to a machine patented by Osmond Blunden four years earlier in 1891, which processed peat by mashing, to produce tubes of quick drying peat with good burning properties; the same result that Morison had achieved by using manpower some thirty years previously. He was, as ever, full of hope for the development of peat utilisation: 'If by Blunden's Process now advocated the Manual Labour is Minifyed, There can be no dought but the Peat Problem is solved.'

Donald never forgot the Lewis Chemical Works. His manuscript, written in 1895 just prior to his death, is a passionate document forged with a deep conviction about what had happened three decades earlier. Donald had the ability to soothe people. Attracted by his simple, direct intellect and intelligent mind they confided in him, giving him an intimate awareness of the involvement of those with whom he worked. The title of the manuscript, 'The Beginning and the end of the Lewis Chemical Works, 1857-1874', seems to suggest the role that Henry Caunter played in the saga as the man who both started the project and who helped to bring about its demise. Morison is never slow to hector Henry despite his obvious affection for the man – he even named one of his children Henry Caunter Morison: 'In this case Caunter had sense but no reason, otherwise an agreeable Gentleman.'

The manuscript has a brooding moodiness about it, driven by the twin themes that Morison weaves throughout the tale. Firstly, there is regret over the wasted expense to Matheson brought about by the mismanagement and failure of an enterprise which Morison saw as capable of success. Secondly, there is regret as to the personal sacrifice of his own established career in order to work for Matheson. Perhaps the manuscript was written out of frustration and anger at what had happened and was an attempt by Donald to set the record straight. There was plenty of fuel for the anger of an old man reflecting on the wasted opportunities of earlier years and the contempt for those who, unlike himself, had no sense of honesty, responsibility, economy, hard graft and service.

Perhaps the writing was a matter of pride for Morison. It was he who had first built the works, he who learned to understand how the process of peat distillation worked and he who adapted and improved the works to make them robust and safe to operate. He must have felt a sense of ownership. After Paul left the works in 1862, Morison was able to fine-tune the process to such an extent that, on returning to the island as a visitor in 1865, Paul described the Lewis Chemical Works as 'the compleatest yet erected for the distillation of hydrocarbon oils from peat.' These were probably words of encouragement to an old friend trying to do his best while surrounded, to paraphrase Paul, 'by an animate chaos'. Paul believed that those working in the chemical industry did not need a broad and deep chemical knowledge: 'It is believed there are a great number of questions of considerable technical importance for the determination of which it is not at all necessary that the operator should be possessed of any greater chemical knowledge than may be assumed by belonging to the occupation in which he is habitually employed.' In other words, one does not need to know how to make cement powder in order to mix cement. Paul would have warmed to Morison with all his native ability, seeing him perhaps as the embodiment of his thoughts.

Donald Morison's sons were all successful in their chosen professions and settled in this country as well as Australia and Canada. The 'Creed Morisons' as the family became known, were spread far and wide. Angus, the eldest son, emigrated to Australia in 1881, while his sons James and Walter both moved to Montreal where James continued in the family profession of stone-mason. Walter took the manuscript with him, and in 1920 sent it to Lord Leverhulme, the then-owner of Lewis, in London for his consideration. Peat distillation was again topical; during World War 1, the exploitation of peat in order to obtain clean, sulphur-free bunkering fuel for naval vessels (recently converted from coal firing) had been discussed by the government. Leverhulme showed only polite but muted interest in the document.

Henry Morison, the son named after Henry Caunter, was to continue the connection between the Caunter name and the Garrabost brickworks into the twentieth century. After the brickworks closed, the land at Claypark was taken over by Kenneth Macleod, a native of Baranahuie, near Stornoway, who was a forester involved with the planting of the trees in the Castle grounds. Kenneth's great-grandson, Alasdair MacIver of Milngavie, had an aunt who was married to Henry Morison. Henry passed away in Weymouth in 1938.

The manuscript next passed back across the Atlantic to St Andrews, where Donald Morison's youngest son, Lieutenant John Morison, had settled with his family and his mother after retiring from the Royal Navy. It was passed in turn to his son, Donald Robertson Morison, who settled in Kingussie and who, encouraged or inspired by his grandfather's exploits in the oil industry, became a student of chemistry at St Andrews University, graduating in 1923. He became a science teacher in Kingussie, where he was also provost from 1957 to 1965. In 1967, he presented the manuscript to the National Library of Scotland for posterity (M/S 9586).

In the early hours of the morning of 2nd March 1897, Donald Morison passed away in Bayhead, in the house where he had been born sixty-eight years earlier. The Highland News reported on the funeral of a much loved man: 'The high esteem in which he was held by all classes of the community was testified by the large and representative concourse that followed his remains to their last resting place in Sandwick Cemetery.'

Donald Morison will always be remembered for his intriguing manuscript, which gives us an insight into the characters inhabiting Lewis in the mid-nineteenth century, into the way the estate operated and into the way of Lewis life during Matheson's tenure of the island.

About five years ago Iain Mitchell, a retired Stornoway businessman who had a deep interest in the history of his native island, commissioned a monument to be erected at the back of the car park opposite the Creed Lodge to mark the existence of the Lewis Chemical Works. James 'Woody' Wood, a local stone-mason, produced an excellent structure incorporating Garrabost bricks, pieces of the tramway track and an information board with an outline of the project. The construction of a path up to the site is planned. Donald Morison would have no doubt been pleased to see that his writings had been appreciated.

Henry Caunter had moved to Stornoway around 1856 when he was in his late forties. With the demise of the Lewis Chemical Works, when he was in his late sixties, he chose to stay on in the town, living in Glen House. Over the years he had become an established member of Stornoway society, renowned for his friendliness and ability. There is no evidence however of Henry pursuing his artistic abilities in Stornoway as he had done in Ashburton, despite these abilities being known to Morison. There is an unsigned oil painting of Sir James Matheson hanging in Dingwall Sheriff Court and Henry would have had plenty of opportunity to realise such a painting. However, expert opinion is that the portrait is probably the work of the Prussian artist, Otto Leyde, who exhibited paintings of Sir James and Lady Matheson at the Royal Academy Exhibition at Edinburgh in 1869.

On the other hand, Henry's other passions, those of music and song, blossomed in Stornoway as they had in Ashburton, no doubt encouraged by the kindred spirit of Lady Mary Jane Matheson. She arranged concerts for Stornoway society in Lews Castle, where local performers entertained with a variety of instrumental and vocal works. In August 1862, the Choral Society of Stornoway was formed with Henry Caunter as president and conductor. The inaugural concert was given in November of that year in the Masonic Halls. It was a sell-out: 'so much was the concert in repute, and so universally favoured by all classes of the community that the tickets were scarcely issued when they were all bought up ... The arrival of Sir James and Lady Matheson and a distinguished party from the castle was a sign for a burst of the warmest applause.'

The eighteen-strong, four-part choir gave a performance which was well-received with many encores demanded. The Inverness Courier correspondent concluded: 'It is we trust the inauguration of a series of musical entertainments. Under the presiding genius of Mr Caunter, a gentleman possessed of the highest musical attainments, they will ever surpass what they have already accomplished.'

The Choral Society, or Choral Union as it became known, gave regular concerts over the following decades with Henry as president, later relinquishing the conductor's baton to Sargeant Craik of the Ross-shire Artillery Volunteers. Performances were well-patronised by the Mathesons and usually given as fund-raisers, supporting the Stornoway Artillery Volunteers, the Ladies' Sanitary Association or the Stornoway Sailors' Home. Occasionally, Lady Matheson would perform at the concerts, singing solos, duetting with Henry Caunter on flute and piano or in leading the choir in the National Anthem. There is evidence that James Matheson was also a flautist; amongst Matheson's letters is one written from Canton to a London supplier requesting flute music by Haydn, Mozart and Pleyel and a collection of national airs. In the 1880s, following Henry's death, the baton was to pass to John Forbes, the rector of the Nicolson Institute. The choir eventually ceased to perform but was rekindled in the late 1970s, by Douglas Leadbitter, as the Stornoway Singers.

Henry never lost his interest in geology. In April 1871, he reported his observations on Lewis erratics – free-standing stones of foreign origin – to the Royal Society of Edinburgh Committee on Boulders and, a couple of years later as the Lewis Chemical Works were winding down, he co-wrote a paper on 'The Geology of the Neighbourhood of Stornoway' which his co-author, James Thomson FGS, read to the Geological Society of Glasgow.

When Henry became ill with heart disease in the late 1870s, his eldest daughter Sarah, a spinster who had been living with her uncle and aunt MacColl, in Edinburgh, came to live in Millburn cottage, as Glen House was then called, to tend to her father. Henry's last days were spent with his loving daughter close at hand and on the morning of September 15th 1881 he passed away, aged seventy-three. A large crowd gathered at his funeral service which was conducted by the Rev EA Sandford, a close friend of Lady Matheson's, and he was buried in the graveyard of St Peter's Episcopal Church in Stornoway, as reported in the Northern Chronicle and by the Western Times in his native Ashburton:

> He had a long and lingering illness through which he was tenderly and assiduously nursed by his daughter (Miss Caunter). The mortal remains of the deceased were interred ... after an impressive funeral service by the Rev Mr Sandford of England. Lady Matheson, who highly esteemed the deceased, and Miss Caunter were present and placed beautiful wreaths of flowers on the coffin.

Sarah subsequently went to stay at Kirkbuddo Estate, Forfar, with her younger sister Alice and her family. Alice had married James Jackson, Depute Surgeon General of the Indian Medical Service in India in 1869. Tragically however, Alice was widowed young after her husband died in a hunting accident on his estate of Kirkbuddo in Forfar in 1887. Alice had a son, George Erskine, and a daughter, Alice Mabel, neither of whom married. She died in 1916 while Alice Mabel died in 1948, having inherited her grandfather's 'political' gene; in 1933 she had been awarded an OBE for 'political and public service', supporting the Scottish and Unionist party rather than the Liberals.

Upon her death in 1895, Sarah left an estate equivalent to about half a million pounds at today's value. She had enjoyed a private income throughout her whole life and probably inherited considerable wealth from her father whose will, if it ever existed, has not yet been found.

In Stornoway, Henry Caunter had become a well- loved and respected man-about-town. His name is still remembered today by an older generation; the corner in Stornoway where Willowglen Road meets the main road south – the corner where Glen House is situated – is often referred to as 'Caunter's Corner'.

Henry Caunter's last act in connection with the Lewis Chemical Works was typical of the kindness of heart for which he was known. In December 1878, he gave a reference to his one-time tormentor, Hugh MacFadyen, the brother of James, who was trying to obtain work in a tile/brick factory or in the paraffin oil industry.

In the story of the Lewis Chemical Works, Caunter is often recalled as the manager who could not manage, the scientist who could not observe, the character whose sense of responsibility lagged far behind his own ambitions. But for all his failings, Caunter remains a man of massive enthusiasm, energy and curiosity, who not only set up the works but kept them moving forward despite being out of his depth and having to endure the set-backs and deceptions occurring around him. David Crabbe's assessment of Henry's initial and subsequent development of the works reflects the serendipity – an important feature of science – that Caunter seemed to experience: 'Any progress he would make was going to be on the basis of guesswork and good fortune rather than by the application of strongly grasped technical principles.'

Matheson saw his technological developments on Lewis as a means of providing much needed employment for his tenants. Many hundreds were employed in the peat-cutting season, both at the chemical works and at the brick works, but, curiously, census returns show few references to individuals employed at these two concerns.

By 1861, a small community had developed at the Creed Works. There were three labourers working under the foreman Donald Morison: Murdo MacKenzie from Carloway (b. 1840), Donald MacKenzie from Bayble (b.1815) and John MacKay from Lochs (b. 1830). Donald MacKenzie lived in a 'Forrester's Cottage' with his family, Murdo MacKenzie lodging with them. John MacKay and family lived in 'Parafine Works No. 1' with his family, while the larger 'Parafine Works No. 2' was home to Donald Morison and his family. Lodging with the Morisons were the engineman, David Carmichael (b.1835) from Campbeltown – known as an 'enginesmith' – and the tinsmith David Howie (b.1832) from Dundee.

By 1871, there had been a turn-over of staff. Donald Morison and his large family were now living across the road from the Chemical Works in the grand 'Creed P[ark] Lodge', or Creed Lodge as it is called today, a miniature castle of a building complete with castellated roof and small tower, built as a gate-house at the entrance to the Castle grounds. The labouring staff – two men and a woman – lived in the 'Chemical Works Bothy', which was Caunter's original works converted for habitation. They were John Smith from Lochs (b. 1846), Donald MacKinnon from Lochs (b. 1846) and Christina MacKenzie from Stornoway (b. 1817). The 'Creed Paraffine Cottage' appeared as a dwelling in census returns up to 1891 but was probably the 'Chemical Works Bothy' renamed.

At Garrabost, the workforce appeared to be more permanent, although there was still a lot of casual labour during the peat-cutting season, with people coming from as far away as Achmore, twelve miles distant, to earn a few shillings. In 1861 there were four brick-makers named in the census returns: James MacFadyen, William MacLeod (b.1785), Angus MacLeod (b. 1813) and Murdo Graham (b. 1836). Murdo Graham continued as a brick-maker until the works shut in the mid-1880s, whereupon he became a crofter. There were a similar number of workers at the Garrabost site of the Chemical Works: Kenneth MacLeod (b. 1836), Malcolm MacKenzie (b. 1841), Donald MacKay (b. 1847) and John Graham (b.1831), brother of Murdo. Malcolm MacKenzie and Kenneth MacLeod both lived with Dr Paul, being ranked as 'Workmen', whilst Paul was recorded as a 'Gentleman'. William Whithead, the assistant chemist, also lived at Garrabost with his family. A second foreman, surname Laurie, is also thought to have worked at the brickworks at the same time as James MacFadyen according to Alasdair MacIver.

The cooper at Garrabost was George Craig, who had been dismissed for trying to blow the whistle on the shady dealings of MacFadyen. He moved into Stornoway where he became a merchant, opening a grocer's shop in Bayhead. The important job of blacksmith at Garrabost was given to George MacDonald (b. 1831), who had served his apprenticeship at Stornoway. When the Chemical Works closed, he moved back to Stornoway, staying at Keith St and then Lewis St, continuing his profession into the twentieth century.

By 1871, there were six recorded brick-makers at Garrabost: Hugh MacFadyen (b. 1822), foreman and brother of James; John Matheson (b.1819); Alexander MacLeod (b.1827); the brothers John and Murdo Graham and Hugh MacFadyen's sixteen year old daughter Margaret, who was employed as a flower-pot maker. The only recorded entry connected with the Chemical Works at Garrabost is that of Kenneth MacLeod who is noted as an 'Oil Manufacturer'. He had previously lodged with Dr Paul as a workman and had probably picked up enough know-how on oil distilling to enable him to help keep the works alive through the James MacFadyen era.

Murdo Graham of Garrabost and John MacAskill from Lower Bayble were still recorded as brick-makers in 1881.

The brickworks had lasted for a few years beyond that date, according to Kenneth MacLeod of Garrabost, who gave evidence to the Napier Commission in 1883. By that time, Hugh MacFadyen had returned to the mainland and was working as a brick-maker in Partick. The brick-makers became full-time crofters or fishermen after the close of the brickworks.

A chemical works and brick works such as has been described would have required a lot more staff than is recorded here. Perhaps the enumerators missed some households or people were recorded simply as labourers rather than being noted as working at a particular site. Whatever the truth of the matter, the realization of Matheson's hopes for employment for his tenants is a matter of debate. The permanent jobs at the Chemical Works and Brick Works were very expensive to create and sometimes involved bringing specialists in from the mainland. However, the Lewis Chemical Works and the Brick Works did provide casual labour in the form of peat cutting, which would have been a blessing for the hundreds of crofters involved, coming at a lean time in the crofting year. The brief era of lime-burning at the Chemical Works also allowed crofters to pay their rents. The short-lived casual labour of dyke-building and draining for William Smith's Deanston experiment and the opportunity for wages provided by the Ordnance Survey put money into crofters' pockets at a time when it was desperately needed after the disastrous potato famine.

Unfortunately, Matheson's attempts to improve the lives of his tenants with the Brick Works and Chemical Works ended up causing some of them disruption and harsh treatment. When Lord Napier was collecting evidence for his Commission in 1883, which heralded the Crofting Act of 1886, Kenneth MacLeod, the spokesman for Garrabost, was a twenty year old when the Brick Works started in 1844:

When the brick works commenced about 35 years ago in our neighbourhood, the best part of our hill pasture was attached to it. This was made into parks enclosed by turf dykes. These dykes had to be kept in repair until about two years ago without receiving any wages for our labour. Paraffin oil manufacture was also for a time carried on in connection with this brick work, and a stranger who came to superintend it got part of the pasture also [Paul or MacFadyen]; and our peat banks were taken from us for the use of these works, and we had to cut them at a much greater distance from our houses; and some of the peats we cut were carried away without our consent and without payment. One man who cut some in the old place after we were told to give it up, had to pay a fine of £2 and his rent raised ten shillings; and he still pays the increase of rent which was imposed of upwards of twenty years ago. If our cattle or horses entered the parks, even in winter, we had to pay pound money for them. The children who attended the cattle were often ill-used.

The crofters were given no compensation for being deprived of good pasture on which the works were built, and the dykes surrounding the pastures, which crofters had to maintain for no pay, prevented them from easily reaching their well for water. It was not all gloom. Kenneth MacLeod and his fellow crofters were not averse to taking the casual employment that the works offered, although the permanent workers kept the enclosure as their own pasture.

What was James Matheson doing when his chemical enterprise was being developed for the markets and enveloped in deception? It was not in his style to be directly involved with the Lewis Chemical Works. He was a man of position and standing in society; a noble who was above commercial affairs. He supplied the site, the capital and running costs and his name. He chose the most eminent managers and gave them encouragement and unquestioned support, expecting them to get on with the job. His only recorded direct involvement in the day-to-day running of the works occurred when he persuaded Donald Morison to commit to becoming his employee after the latter had tendered his notice, following a disagreement with Caunter over the use of peat gas as a fuel.

The Mathesons, who remained childless, were not rooted in one place, but owned properties throughout the country. As late as 1867, Matheson's empire was still expanding, with the acquisition of Bennetsfield Estate on the Black Isle. According to Richard Grace, Matheson was at one time the second largest landowner in the UK. The couple often moved with the seasons, spending winters abroad in Italy or at Mentone on the fashionable French Riviera. The Mathesons did however spend a considerable amount of time in Lewis, residing three quarters of the year in the Hebrides and the north of Scotland.

When in Lewis, Matheson was a busy man, reading business reports and letters from his factor and others and catching up on the affairs of the estate. He still had an interest in Matheson and Co. of London and was Chairman of the P&O shipping line. If anything of note needed organising within the community, he was the chairman, whether it be letters of condolence to a widowed Queen, overseeing Education Association exams, chairing public lectures or presiding over Committees for Sanitary

Improvement and the Harbour Commission. He was continually involved in the well-being of folk, as he had been since the potato famine of 1846. Whenever disaster struck he would react; despatching a vessel with supplies for homeward-bound fishermen stranded in the creeks of Cape Wrath or providing relief after the Great Storm of 1869. When there were happy times the Mathesons shared their joy. On the occasion of their silver wedding anniversary in 1868, cattle were slaughtered to provide fresh meat, along with tea and sugar, as gifts for the castle workers and the poor folk of the town.

His seemingly care-free life wasn't without distraction however, as the press reported in October 1865: 'Charles Gustaldi ... and Joseph Newman ... charged with burglariously breaking and entering the residence of Sir James Matheson of Cleveland Row [London] ... valuable property was carried off.'

Matheson was very conscious of his public duty in the wider world and did not retire as MP for Ross-shire until 1868, by which time he was seventy-two. As at Ashburton, he made way for a relative, and his nephew, Alexander Matheson of Ardross, was duly elected. In 1866, James Matheson had been appointed Lord Lieutenant of Ross-shire, and was presented to Queen Victoria when she visited the county in 1872. In 1870 he retired as chairman of Tain Academy and reduced his involvement in railway companies.

Matheson continued to try and improve communications between Lewis and the mainland. Aided by his mother-in-law, Mrs Percival, he lobbied the Post Office for an improved postal service to and from the island. In 1867 there were only two mail boats a week and the commerce of the town, one in which the number of inhabitants doubled to ten thousand in the fishing season, suffered as a result of constant delays in correspondence, not just with mainland Britain but with European cities involved with the fishing trade. Mrs Percival wrote a pamphlet on the matter, but by November 1868 the Post Office had still not taken action and Matheson chaired a public meeting to address the matter. The steamer service had become so irregular that the mail boat had sometimes departed Stornoway before the mails had even been delivered. Making prompt replies and closing business deals was a nightmare; another problem for Henry Caunter. A daily service was requested, as was the case for the Orkney Islands, so that business might flourish.

A month later, the significance of the latest development in communication technology – the telegraph – was not lost on Matheson. There were grumblings from local businessmen who were again suffering at the hands of the Post Office due to the lack of telegraph facilities in Stornoway, although it was available in places equally remote but less commercially important. Matheson offered to guarantee revenue as the Northern Ensign reported in December 1869: 'the Lews with its tens of thousands of inhabitants, its all valuable and rising fishing interests, and its importance as a port of call for foreign shipping, is left out in the cold. Here again the proprietor reads the department [the Post Office] a lesson, Sir James having offered a personal guarantee of £300 a year revenue.'

Earlier that year technical innovation in the building industry was being championed by Matheson by the construction of walls in Stornoway using the patent process of Mr Tall from London. In 1865 Tall had taken out a patent for the use of wooden shuttering in the construction of walls made from concrete. He had successfully used his method to build two-storey houses in London, some of which still stand today. Matheson used Tall's patent method to construct garden walls; one of the developments which attracted the attention of HRH Prince Arthur during his visit to Stornoway in June 1869. In a lecture on the improvement of crofters' houses given by George Brooke and chaired by Matheson in the Stornoway Masonic Hall in September of that year, the lecturer suggested: 'as timber is scarce, the new mode of building with concrete now adopted by Sir James Matheson could be taken advantage of for the dwelling houses of the fishermen.'

Is this what prompted the poured concrete method of house and wall construction, using aggregate from the shore, which is commonly found in Lewis? According to Norman MacLeod of Knock, it was a common practice in the early half of the last century, when building a house, to buy the timber for the roof sarking first. This planking was used as shuttering for building the poured concrete walls. Indeed, the author was mystified, until he heard this tale, as to why a thin layer of cement could be seen in the attic, on the inside of the sarking of his own dwelling, built in the 1930s. As many of the small cottages and walls still in existence on the island attest, poured concrete walls are certainly strong and long-lasting.

By the late 1860s, Matheson was funding many improvements in Stornoway, although some were contentious: a new pier and harbour works, the widening of Point Street, North Beach Street and Harbour Lane, the replacement of old tenements by new, work on the embankment of North Beach Street and Cromwell Street and the creation of Percival Square as a public market place complete with a fountain by courtesy of Mrs Percival.

All this hectic activity left little time for an intimate interest in the comings and goings of the Lewis Chemical Works. No doubt Henry Caunter kept Matheson well informed, when in residence, of all the developments, patent applications, new products, research trials and so on. Failures and deceptions would not be mentioned and there was no over-seeing board of management to investigate production problems, issue market reports and draw up financial accounts, forward plans and the like.

Matheson was an old man of seventy-eight and in poor health when the kilns of his Chemical Works were extinguished. Just a few years later he passed away at Mentone on the 31st December 1878. He was eighty-two years old. The obituary notices followed, full of tales of 'munificence', 'the nobility and unselfishness' of a man who made Lewis 'bloom and blossom as the rose', an 'exceptionally good and improving landlord' whose 'exertions to provide the inhabitants of the island of Lews with food during the famine of 1847' led to 'Mr Matheson of Achany blossoming into Sir James Matheson of The Lews'. He was buried at Lairg in Sutherland, where Lady Matheson erected a large monument to a bold life.

Reminders of the Mathesons pervade Stornoway, whose harbour is dominated by the Castle, at last being restored to life as a museum and up-market holiday accommodation. The woodlands and grounds are a haven for wildlife and is a recreational heaven for walking, running, cycling, golfing, rugby, football and fishing. Matheson Road, the Matheson Building at The Nicolson Institute and Percival Square are some of the public places in the town where the Matheson name lives on.

Throughout his tenure of Lewis, the popular press, in news items and articles and in travel guides, championed the improvements that Matheson brought to Lewis: roads, bridges, schools and teachers, land reclamation, stock improvement, opportunity of employment, gas works, water works, buildings of all types from castles and lodges to schools, manses, fish curing houses, brick works, chemical works, quays, and the patent slip. They applauded his constant charity, his giving of gifts and money and his seeking to ensure that times of want were addressed. They rejoiced when he was lauded, but there is always another side to the coin and others had always seen things differently.

Despite all the money that Matheson had ploughed into Lewis, the well-being of his tenants, especially those outwith Stornoway, had not materially improved in the thirty years of his tenure of the estate. In February of 1862, just a few weeks before Horatio Paul left Lewis, Donald MacKay, a shoemaker in Stornoway wrote to his son-in-law, James Campbell: 'This place is quite gone. The people were never in such a destitute state in general. There is no work of any kind doing, even the shoemakers are going idle and families are on the brink of starvation for want of employment and as there is no prospect of any change to the better they will not get credit.'

In 1874, Matheson finally, if reluctantly, removed Donald Munro from the office of factor and replaced him with a Commissioner, Hugh M Matheson of Edinburgh, who ran the business of the estate from afar with the help of a local agent, MacKay, who had been Munro's clerk. In March 1878, some nine months before Matheson's death, a long letter was written to Hugh Matheson published under the title 'Island of Lews and its fishermen crofters' enquiring about the management of the estate and laying bare many home truths concerning James Matheson. The letter was written by Donald MacKinlay, who was born and educated in Stornoway and who rose to be a managing partner of a mercantile firm in India, at one time being elected as President of the Bengal Chamber of Commerce. He was well-versed in management matters and he knew the character of the Lewisman. Upon retirement, he leased the Gress Shootings in the Back area of Lewis. MacKinlay quotes one 'intelligent native' who had lived his whole life on the island and who, in 1874, had remarked: 'I have no hesitation in saying that the Lews tenants are in a much worse condition now than at any time during my memory.'

Things were definitely not as they appeared to the casual observer. Although Matheson had tried to address major problems and succeeded in many cases, his failures were a result of his personal failings; his inability to enter into dialogue with the crofters and the implicit trust he placed in his managers to do their job without question. According to W. Anderson Smith, who reflected on Matheson's management in 1886, shortly after his death: 'No doubt the instruments he employed were frequently useless, but he was nevertheless responsible for having used them. His Eastern habit of mind, his impatience of adverse views or adverse criticism prevented any wholesale discussion of his measures or any public opinion being brought to bear upon his administration.'

One of the 'instruments' Matheson employed was the factor Donald Munro, whose rule so severely oppressed and depressed the tenants. Munro ran the estate according to his own whim, his confidence boosted by Matheson's refusal to hear anything against him. His loyalty to Munro demonstrated a trait of Matheson's character; a desire to trust and support his captains. As Richard Grace has indicated, this loyalty was well in evidence in his business dealings out East. However, Munro often acted without reference to Matheson. MacKinlay is succinct: 'He [Munro] had so wormed himself into the confidence of the proprietor, that he was allowed to "manage" the people and the estate without any control (very much as he pleased); and he ruled over all with a rod of iron. The crofter "tenants-at-will" were quite at his mercy and nothing was done to improve their material condition.'

Under Munro's regime fear stalked the land as he rigidly applied the complex estate rules, known as the Articles of

Set of 1849 or 'Lewis Magna Carta', which sought to order and control the crofters' every act. W. Anderson Smith stated: 'We are told that at one time the cottars were offered leases with only fifty four rules attached, the transgression of one cancelling the right of the lessee. One old man, at Ness, laughed heartily at the document; sagely remarking that he could not keep ten commandments for a mansion in the sky, much less fifty four for a black house in the Lews.'

Munro's actions undoubtedly caused the crofters to question their trust in their landlord and soured their affection for him. In 1883, Kenneth MacLeod of Garrabost, who gave testimony to the Napier Commission about the effects of the development of the Garrabost Brick Works on the crofting land, let his feelings be known: 'We were so much afraid of estate people that we were afraid if we did not do what they liked ... we should be deprived of the small holding we had ... We are so depressed that fear of estate management and the like of that has taken the courage out of us.'

In August 1858, an article had appeared in the Northern Ensign. A positive report on Matheson's improvements in Lewis noted one very important failing when considering his model farm near Stornoway and Lewis agriculture generally: 'On this farm and the ground around the Castle, much employment is given to the people who are engaged in trenching, draining, road making etc. This is however, an exception to the agriculture on the island. Still there are no written leases without which the tenants have no confidence in enjoying the fruits of their labours.' The Ensign correspondent noted one croft which stood out in terms of crop condition, croft layout and the comfort of the croft house. It proved to be the croft of one Finlay MacLean, one of a small number of crofters who had managed to obtain leases. He had demonstrated for all to see just what the crofter was capable of achieving, given the opportunity:

> The little man was exceedingly proud of showing us his cross-drains, main-drains and pieces of moor he had brought under cultivation each year and what he proposed to do in further improving the little farm ... No proprietor could take greater pride in showing off his grounds than did Finlay on this occasion, the secret of whose activity is manifestly in his lease.

Croft house improvement was applauded by Matheson as John Munro MacKenzie reported to the Napier Commission: 'We drove to the house, a distance of 12 miles. Sir James was surprised and delighted with the house to see it so well built by the crofter. He wished the occupants much happiness in their new abode and he hoped many of the neighbours would follow his example.'

Despite incentives, this improvement was scarce. Under Munro's regime, crofters feared being removed from an improved dwelling to make way for a tenant paying higher rents, with no reparations being given for the improvements. There was simply no incentive for them to put extra money and effort into something which would be taken from them.

The wealth of the crofters lay in their own ability, and their understanding of and affinity for the land, not in slavishly following rules and what they saw as pointless innovations and developments. Some Lewis crofters did however appreciate Matheson and his spending on the island, as the correspondent from the Inverness Advertiser pointed out in October 1852: 'Sir James is deservedly adored by the inhabitants of Lewis; and those crofters who can speak English in their homely and endearing language call him 'Jamie pay for a'!' Matheson had the potential to be a landlord who was true to his first hopeful words on visiting the island: 'Our task in the interior will be more difficult but I see no cause to despair.' But by pouring money into his sometimes misplaced industrial schemes, Matheson missed the chance of lifting the beating heart of the crofting community of Lewis. In his failure to abide by the Royal Society motto, 'Take no-one's word for it', Matheson allowed his managers to do as they willed and so apply their own narrative to history.

Thus it was that Henry Caunter, introduced as manager by Donald Munro when Matheson was in London, was allowed to chart the rocky course of the Lewis Chemical Works, not allowing it to reach its potential. John Munro MacKenzie had had his feet firmly on the ground when advising Matheson in the early 1850s, as MacKinlay, with conviction, pointed out to Hugh Matheson just three years after the works ceased: 'The Chemical Works, as has been observed, were executed contrary to the advise of Mr Munro MacKenzie and the result has confirmed the wisdom of his opinion. He saw clearly at the time that, without benefiting anyone, they would in the end, as they have done, prove a complete loss to the proprietor.'

The story of the Lewis Chemical Works is a reflection of life in general in Lewis at the time of Matheson's ownership of the island; a time of hope, promise and expectation on the surface but with a strong undercurrent of despair and failure ever present. A time of 'enormous, reckless blunders'. In the other world of 'if only', Lewis could indeed have been a different place if James Matheson had been a little wiser in his choice of managers. Captain Newall, writing in 1889 of his sporting adventures in Lewis, recalled a tale about Matheson, in which the proprietor did briefly deal directly with a crofter's problem, with a good result:

It is related that on one occasion the late proprietor, Sir J Matheson, was driving along the road when he espied a man at this burn busily engaged in capturing the spawning trout. So intent was he on his poaching that he was not aware of the presence of the enemy. Sir James got out and stalked the man, and himself seized him *'flagrante delicto'*. No doubt the fellow was considerably astonished to find into who's hands he had fallen, when he recognised in his captor the kindly face and commanding stature of the 'proprietor'. I believe he escaped with nothing more than a whigging, on the plea that as he, Sir James, was himself the captor, he was constrained to treat the case leniently.

Epilogue

The arrival of oil did not signal the end of commercial interest in peat. Periodically, the Government produced reports on the usage of peat and peat products and industry continued to try and exploit the vast resource. During the first decade of the twentieth century, over 100 patents were filed concerning methods of utilising peat.

On Dartmoor, there were repeated attempts to distil peat for coke or gas, culminating, in 1943, in plans to pipe bunkering fuel oil, obtained by distillation of peat on the moor, directly to the naval shipyards at Devonport. The charcoal produced would be used in gas masks. Alas, all were unsuccessful.

In Ireland, interest in peat continued at high levels; in the early 1900s, a Bill was proposed in Parliament to grant powers for the production of peat gas to fuel electricity generation, but came to nothing. Determination prevailed however, leading to the formation, in 1936, of Bord na Mona – the Irish Peat Board – which supplies peat to power stations in Ireland to this day.

On the continent, peat distillation was pursued for gas production, for electricity generation, and for making high quality coke for the steel industry. In 1905, the factory at

Beuerberg in Bavaria was the most up-to-date, marketing all the products of peat distillation.

After the Matheson era, Lewis was eventually sold to Lord Leverhulme, another rich industrial magnate, who had big plans to develop the island's fishing industry after World War 1. This required the land to be farmed in order to provide for a sustainable workforce. The scheme, although practical on paper, foundered as again the imposition of foreign ideas did not find favour with the Lewis crofters who simply wanted to pursue their dream of a few acres to sustain themselves.

Lewis peat remained a source of curiosity for the rich. In 1928, TB MacAulay, sometime president of the Sun Life Assurance Company of Canada and a wealthy ex-patriot of the Uig district of the island, poured money into Scotland. He financed Memorial halls, a Widows' Fund, Educational Trust Funds, The MacAulay Soil Research Institute at Aberdeen, the Animal Behavioural Research Department at Edinburgh University and schemes in his native island. On Lewis he gave money to the public library in Stornoway, to the Lewis Hospital and the Town Hall Building Fund and, to help ease the economic situation on the island, he gifted £10,000 for the setting up of an experimental farm – the MacAulay farm, literally across the road from the site of the Lewis Chemical Works. Peatland was drained and the soil cultivated for crops, dairy farming and poultry but, although results were initially promising, it was not a success.

The peat of Lewis was not forgotten as a source of energy. A final hurrah of exploitation in 1981 saw plans proposed by the Scottish Peat and Land Development Association for a peat-fuelled power station at Stornoway, drawing fuel from the Barvas Moor just to the west of the town. As a back-up fuel, quick-growing alder and birch trees would be grown on the cleared ground. The facility would repay the £4 million capital costs within twelve years and run at about half the cost of the diesel-powered generators then in operation. A later connection to the National Grid through Skye saw the end of notions for large-scale energy production from peat on Lewis, although energy production from the wind could take its place if the sub-sea connector cable to the mainland ever arrives.

The 'day of the peat' belongs now to the few who, each May, delight in the simple joy of 'going to the peats'.

References

Newspapers/Magazines/Periodicals
Inverness Courier
Inverness Advertiser
Highland News
John O'Groat Journal
Glasgow (Daily) Herald
Edinburgh Advertiser
Oban Times
Morning Chronicle
The Standard
The Daily News
The Times
The Morning Post
The Evening Standard
Pall Mall Gazette
The Daily Post
Illustrated London News
Western Times
North Devon Journal
Woolmer's Exeter and Plymouth Gazette
Trewman's Exeter Flying Post
Western Flying Post, Sherbourne and Yeovil Mercury
White's Devonshire Directory of 1850
Cambridge Chronicle
Norfolk News
Liverpool Mercury
Celtic Magazine No. 83, Sept 1882, Vol. 7
Stornoway Historical Society Magazine, Dec 2010/11
Back In the Day, Stornoway Gazette, 2009/10
The Rudhach
Harper's Monthly, 1875
Household Words, 1851
The Freeman's Journal, 1851
The Examiner, 1857

The Graphic, 1889
The Spectator
The Gentleman's Magazine
Clay Park Bricks, No. 1, 2006

Public Records
National Records Office
Scotland's People
Patents Office
Census returns 1841 – 1901 Scotland/England
Valuation Rolls for Ross and Cromarty
Report of the Royal Commission for the Condition of Crofters
  (Napier Commission)
New Statistical Account 1844
Ordnance Survey Name Book 1847
Post Office Annual Glasgow Directory, 1867-1872
Hansard
H.M. Report; Destructive Distillation of Peat 1851
H.M. Report; Manufacture of Fuel ... and other Products of Peat
  1893
H.M.Report; Molasses and Peat Fodder 1897

Scientific Institution/Historical Society Records
Royal Geographical Society records
Royal Society records and Proceedings
Journal of Chemical Education, 1936
Pharmaceutical Journal, 1849/50/51/56/58/59
Chemist and Druggist, 1902/1917
Journal of the Society of Arts, 1864/70
Proceedings of the Royal Dublin Society, 1907
Reports; meetings of the British Association for the Advancement
  of Science, 1862/1908
Pharmaceutical Journal and Pharmacist, 1917
Journal of the Chemical Society, 1918
Chemical News, 1862
Annals of Science, 1978
Royal Society of Edinburgh; Committee on Boulders publication,

1872

Transactions of the Newcomen Society, Vol. 71, 1999

Transactions of the Devonshire Association, 1966/1896

Transactions of the National Association for the Promotion of Social
Science, 1880

Journal of the Cork Historical and Archaeological Society, 1941

Scottish History Society Journal, 1978

Proclamations of the Philosophical Society of Glasgow, 1867

Handbook of the International Exhibition, 1862

Scottish Peat and Land Development Association; Lewis Peat-fuelled
Power Station Proposals, 1981

Websites

www.archive.org

www.nationalarchives.gov.uk

www.britishnewspaperarchive.co.uk

www.thetimes.co.uk/archive

archive.scotsman.com

www.oldashburton.co.uk

www.brickdirectory.co.uk

artuk.org

www.devonassoc.org.uk

www.ambaile.org.uk

royalsociety.org

www.rpharms.com

Bibliography

Anderson, G., Guide to the Highlands and Islands, 1850

Amery, P.F.S., Sketch of Ashburton and the Woollen Trade, 1876

Ashmore, P., Calanais, The Standing Stones, Urras nan Tursachan, 1995

Asimov, I., Biographical Encyclopadia of Science and Technology, London, 1975

Bischof, G., Elements of Chemical and Physical Geology, London, 1854

Bjorling, P.R. and Gissing, F.T., Peat: its Use and Manufacture, London, 1907

Bornand, O., The Edited Diary of W.M. Rossetti 1870-1873, Oxford, 1977

Carlyle, T. , Past and Present

Cunningham, P., The Castles of the Lews, Acair, Stornoway, 2008

Dawson, A., So Foul and Fair a Day, Birlinn, Edinburgh, 2009

Encyclopaedia Britannica, Eighth Edition, Edinburgh, 1857

Fleet, C., Wilkes, M. and Withers, C.W.J., Mapping the Nation, Birlinn, Edinburgh, 2012

Fredeman, W., The Correspondence of Dante Gabriel Rossetti, 1835-1862, Oxford, 1975

Fredeman, W., The Pre-Raphaelite Brotherhood Journal: William Michael Rossetti's Edited Diary of the Pre-Raphaelite Brotherhood, 1849-1853, Oxford, 1975

Gaunt, W., The Pre-Raphaelite Dream, London, 1942

Gekie, Sir A. LLD FRS, Life of Sir R. I. Murchison, Vol. 1., London, 1875

Gissings, F.T., Commercial Peat; its Uses and Possibilities, London, 1909

Grace, R.J., Opium and Empire, London, 2015

Grant, J.G., A Shilling for Your Scowl, Acair, Stornoway, 1992

Harris, H., The Industrial Archaeology of Dartmoor, David and Charles, Newton Abbot, 1968

Hanham, H.J., Ashburton, a Parliamentary Borough, 1640-1868, Trans. Devonshire Assoc., Vol. 98, 1966

Headrick, J., Report on the Island of Lewis, 1800

Holmes, R., The Age of Wonder, Harper Press, London, 2008

Hutton, G., Shale Oil, a History of the Industry in the Lothians, Ayrshire, 2010

Kerr, W.A., Peat and its Products, Glasgow, 1905

Keswick, M. (Ed.), The Thistle and the Jade, London, 1982

Kingzett, C.T., Chemical Encyclopaedia, London, 1928

Lawson, W., Lewis – the West Coast in History and Legend, Birlinn, Edinburgh, 2008

MacKay, C., It must be Stornoway, Argyll, 2008

MacGillivray, W., A Hebridean Naturalist's Journal Edited by Dr R. Ralph, Acair, Stornoway, 1996

MacKinlay, D., Island of Lews and its Fishermen Crofters, London, 1878

MacDonald, D., Lewis – A History of the Island, Edinburgh, 1978

MacKenzie, J.M., Diary 1851 (edited by J.S. Grant), Acair, Stornoway, 1994

Mills, E.J., Destructive Distillation; a Manualette, London, 1883

Morison, D., The Beginning and the End of the Lewis Chemical Works, 1857-1874, Manuscript held in the National Library of Scotland Edinburgh, MS 9586

Muspratt, J.S., Chemistry; theoretical, practical and analytical, 1860

Newall, Capt. J.T., Scottish Moors and Indian Jungles, London, 1889

Paul, B.H., Manual of Technical Analysis, London, 1857

Payen, Industrial Chemistry edited by B.H.Paul PhD, London, 1878

Pearson, Rev J.B., The Representatives of the Borough of Ashburton, Trans. Devonshire Assoc. Vol. 28, 1896

Pilkington, Dr F., Ashburton; the Dartmoor Town, Devon Books, 1989

Read, J., Humour and Humanism in Chemistry, London, 1947

Rossetti, W.M., Dante Gabriel Rossetti; Letters and Memoir, London, 1895

Rossetti, W.M., Some Reminiscence, London, 1906

Smith, W.A., Lewisiana, London, 1875

Ure, A., Dictionary of Arts, Manufactures and Mines, 1851

Wagner, R., A Handbook of Chemical Technology, London, 1872

Weld, C. R., Vacations in Ireland, London, 1857

Wright, W.H.F., West Country Poets: their lives and works, London 1896

Wood, E., Peatbogs, Plague and Potatoes, Luath, Edinburgh, 2009

Worth, G., James Hannay: his Life and Works, London, 1964

About the Author

Born in London but brought up in Bristol, Ali Whiteford comes from a family of engineers going back four generations. As he grew up he was surrounded by the engineering wonders of Brunel; docks, railways, steamships, and of course the famous Clifton suspension bridge. As a result he developed an abiding interest in 18th and 19th century engineering – and 20th century British motorcycles! He attended Bristol Cathedral School, where he was introduced to Chemistry, afterwards going north to study the subject for a degree at Edinburgh University, where he also undertook a PhD in Chemistry. Ali married a Border lass and they went further north, to the Isle of Lewis where he taught Chemistry for thirty years at the Nicolson Institute in Stornoway, and raised a family of three girls. Now retired, Ali spends his time gardening, cutting peats and making and restoring musical instruments and the odd clock.